Ballad of my Fearless Heroine

Ballad of my Fearless Heroine

Cancer, Be Not Proud

BY VLADIMIR TSESIS

Disclaimer

This book is a work of nonfiction. Unless otherwise noted, the author and the publisher make no explicit guarantees as to the accuracy of the information contained in the book. For reasons of privacy in the majority of cases, names of people and places have been altered to protect their identity. The positive and the negative issues we ran into could happen at any hospital, so I did not feel it was necessary to point fingers.

PALMETTO
PUBLISHING

Charleston, SC
www.PalmettoPublishing.com

Ballad of my Fearless Heroine

First Edition

Paperback ISBN: 978-1-68515-960-3
eBook ISBN: 978-1-68515-961-0

Margaret I never forget your amazing husband David who together with Marina are with God

Dedicated to women, lionhearted heroines with breast cancer,
who meet the enemy as real warriors, who fight and eventually defeat
a powerful adversary in a spiritual battle.

To our wonderful friend of many years to Margaret (Margie) Reid for her friendship, for her prayers, for her humanity who comes from God on Heaven

With best wishes

5/14/2022 Vladim [signature]

Table of Contents

INTRODUCTION

A Bolt from the Blue

As had been my habit for a long time, on Friday, September 22, 2005, I returned home from work at seven o'clock in the evening. My wife, Marina, met me with a kiss and returned to the kitchen to prepare our supper. Soon, like two birds, my Dulcinea del Toboso and I, her medieval knight, were nestled side by side at the table that stood opposite the TV. We watched the *Sanford and Son* sitcom and exchanged our news about the day that had passed, enjoying the quiet and calm of the evening. We were almost done with dessert, and the TV turned off, when Marina set down her fork. "I forgot to tell you, Vovka," she said. "Early in the evening, I received a call from Memorial Hospital. I had my yearly mammogram there. So, the radiologist told me on the phone that he wants me to return to the radiology department. He said he noticed something suspicious on my left-breast mammography film." There was no sign of worry in her calm and dispassionate tone of voice.

However, I felt as if the ground was slipping from under my feet. Any time when Marina had her annual mammogram, I anxiously awaited the results. Since we had known each other, ever since we were teenagers, I knew she had a fibroadenoma in her breast. A fibroadenoma is a painless, benign, noncancerous breast tumor that is solid, not fluid-filled, lump. But in rare cases, fibroadenomas contain breast tissue cells that are predisposed to cancer. Marina's fibroadenoma consisted of dense breast tissue and several lumps that were smooth and moved easily under the skin upon touching. Every previous year when the results of the mammography did not show anything suspicious, I celebrated. But Marina's reaction was always carefree. By nature, she was an optimistic person, for whom the glass was always half full. I was just surprised at her obvious denial of reality. Loving her and never willing to argue with her in her daredevil attitude, I did not want to persuade her to give me more news than she had told me.

As a physician myself, I knew that malignant diseases are an inescapable evil among human beings and that any person, especially of an advanced age, has a chance to have cancer. Nevertheless, I did not want to push Marina. She was smart and mature, and if she consciously or unconsciously denied the reality, I let it be so, as long as it served her well. As for me, just thinking the word *cancer*—a condition that, despite the best treatment and care, in significant numbers of cases gradually chokes the victims with its clutching tentacles—produces anxiety and fear.

I asked Marina what it was exactly that the radiologist had told her.

"Oh, nothing special," she replied. "I just need to be reevaluated with a procedure I forget the name of now. Stop worrying, Vovka. Look at yourself; you look pale. Believe me, it is nothing special. Doctors are calling patients for reevaluation all the time."

"You're right. I shouldn't be worried," I agreed aloud. "When are you supposed to go back for reevaluation? I will accompany you."

"I do not think you should come with me. Personally, I do not expect anything unusual will happen, but if you insist, how can I refuse your company?" She gave me a charming smile and then served me another cup of coffee.

CHAPTER 1

A Woman Named Marina

Girl in a Polka-Dotted Swimsuit

Before turning to the main subject of the book, it might be useful to know more about the heroine of this book.

Marina and I met by sheer accident in the famous city of Odessa in August 1962, when I was twenty-one years old and a fifth-year medical student at Kishinev Medical School. Kishinev (Chișinău) had always been the capital city of Moldova, which at that time was part of the former Soviet Union. Usually, I spent summer vacation with my parents at their home in the Moldovan city of Beltsy. Beltsy was where I was born in 1941 and where I graduated from high school. During vacations, I read, listened to music, rode a bicycle, and met with my friends there. In the evening, especially on weekends, I went to the outdoor dance floor in the main city park. I was not popular among girls at all; they hardly ever showed interest in me.

One August day, I was walking in the town square, and there I met my good school friend, Abram Levin. The medical school where he studied was in Kemerovo, a large industrial city in the southeast of Western Siberia.

"Listen, Vovka," he told me. "The day after tomorrow, my father and I are taking the train to Odessa to have a fun time. Come with us. Imagine, we will sunbathe and swim in the Black Sea."

I did not refuse. Why not accept such a tempting offer? I had studied hard at my medical school, and now I deserved to have time to relax. But what was I going to say to my parents, who wanted me to be with them at home? It did not take me long to come up with a plan. That evening before I went to bed, I told my parents that I must take a test on pharmacology at my medical school. I promised to be back home in four or five days. Overall, I was an honest son, so my parents did not suspect that I was telling them a lie. I justified my unusual behavior by telling myself that if I told them the truth, they would not allow me to take the trip. I knew I was wrong in my deception, but I was young, and I was looking for adventure. Besides, I was burning with desire to visit the legendary and popular Odessa resort city. My parents, whose highest dream was for me to become a doctor, had no objection to my traveling to take the fictional test. Right away they provided me with a modest amount of money and wished me the best.

In two days, Abram, his father, and I arrived in Odessa in the morning. We enjoyed a beautiful sunny day at Langeron Beach, one of the most popular beaches in Odessa. After three great days on this beach, Abram, whose nickname was Abrasha said that the next day he and his father were planning to meet friends from Beltsy at another pleasant beach, Chaika, located along Odessa's famous Big Fountain area.

Arriving to the Chaika beach at exactly the appointed time, 11:00 a.m., I went to the place where Abram and his father were supposed to be. Walking slowly and looking around at the abundance of beautiful girls, I did not have any idea that very soon my fate would be sealed, that I would meet my future faithful friend, my beloved partner of more than half a century of happy marital life.

As I approached the beach, I saw Abram and his father swimming in the sea. The moment Abram saw me, he beckoned me to join them. Since the changing cabins were not set up at that time on the beach, putting on a bathing suit presented a problem. Using a towel and assuming several funny acrobatic poses, I eventually put on my bathing suit, then right away entered the water. Spending a good hour swimming, the Levins and I got out and returned to our spot on the sandy beach. Instead of drying off with towels, we allowed the rays of the bright August sun to dry our bodies.

"You are probably wondering where the acquaintances from our city are, that I promised would be here," Abram said while we were sunbathing. "Don't worry. They went to buy ice cream and soda and will be back soon." Indeed, as my friend promised, in ten minutes, an adult woman and three teenage girls walked up. Three of them I knew from our home city. The woman was Anna Efimovna Sokolovsky, and the fourteen-year-old girl was her daughter, Zhanna. The other teenage girl's name was Zina Samoylov; she was fifteen and the daughter of a well-known physician in Beltsy. The fourth member of the group, a beautiful young woman in a brown polka-dotted bathing suit, who was older than the other two girls, I did not know.

When my friend, Abram, introduced me, all the women replied with an unenthusiastic "Hello."

I had an interesting book with me to read, but a natural desire to chat with pretty girls took over. The most logical choice to talk with was Zina Samoylov. She lived near my house, but she was fifteen, five years younger than me. After several unsuccessful attempts, I understood that Zina was not interested in communicating with me. Since my attempts were in vain, not willing to waste my time, I gave up, and pulling out a book from my bag, I immersed myself in reading. Half an hour passed, and to my surprise, I realized that the girl in the brown polka-dotted swimsuit had been interrupting my reading over and over again, modestly but firmly addressing me with innocent questions. Gradually, I became involved in a conversation with her, and it did not take long for me to notice that this girl was sincerely interested in our conversation. Our conversation became even more interesting when I learned that she liked reading as much as I did. We began to talk about books we had read, about the cities where we lived, about our favorite foods, and the sports we loved. With each minute I found more natural beauty in my conversational partner until it appeared to me that she was the most beautiful young woman I had ever met. The most outstanding features of her face were her magnificent, expressive, dark-brown eyes, her full, rosy lips, and her outstanding lustrous skin.

The name of the girl was Marina, and at nineteen, she was just two years younger than me. Imperceptibly, we separated ourselves from the rest of the group and spent the rest of the day in each other's company. When night came, we parted, only to meet up again the next day. Nobody before had been so attentive to me as my new acquaintance, and in a short time, we became close friends. While I was a clumsy lover, my hovering angel visibly enjoyed satisfying my small needs and wishes. This attitude toward me was completely new for me. I could not understand what this incredible girl found in me, a shy and awkward boy from a provincial town, while the girl I'd met on the shores of the Black Sea was the most beautiful, intelligent, charming, and modest of all the women I had ever met before.

On the second day of our acquaintance, I developed an earache from diving in the sea, which I mentioned to Marina in passing. Saying nothing, she left me and returned in ten minutes, holding a vial of boric acid in her hand. She ordered me to tilt my head, and with the help of a dropper, she slid the boric acid drops into my ear canal. I noticed that in the process, her girlish face shone with a motherly expression. Her treatment cured me at once. Where she was able to find medication on a public beach remained a never-resolved secret. Next day, she became concerned about my sunburn. This time she brought--again, who knows from where--a skin cream, which she applied on my back with tender care.

At noon we parted, agreeing to meet again in the evening. Leaving Marina, I went via public transportation to the apartment I had rented and returned to her at 7:00 p.m. When I was approaching the place of date, from the window of the tram, I saw Marina dressed in a light-violet dress. She was sitting on a bench at the tram stop, and what she was doing pleased my heart; she was immersed in reading a book. The book, I learned a minute later, was by my favorite author, Oscar Wilde. Reading was my main hobby, and I was happy that I was lucky to meet a kindred soul who shared my passion for books.

And so, my vacation transformed from unremarkable into the unforgettable time when I, for the first and last time in my life, fell in love. The girl from the beach was the most splendid creature I had ever met in my life. Why this beautiful and smart Odessa girl had fallen in love with me is still an unsolved puzzle. While she was alive, I asked her this question many times. In response, she would just smile mysteriously not looking at me, never giving me a straight answer. Well aware of my many flaws and failures, I perceived her love as something that should not be taken for granted but as a precious gift from heaven.

Our first encounter lasted only four days. When I returned home, and later to my medical school in Kishinev, I did not dare to believe that what had happened in Odessa could have any future. With each day, I believed less and less that such a wonderful young lady as Marina could ever be genuinely interested in me. After all, we lived in different cities and had known each other for only a limited number of days. Also, she belonged to a higher economic class than I did, which back then meant a lot in choosing a friend. I did not have a high opinion of myself, while in my eyes, Marina was an extraordinary girl, and I did not feel I deserved her. When we said goodbye, we promised to write letters to each other, but I thought that writing a letter to my accidental friend would be only a waste of time.

I might have forgotten about my exciting encounter at the Black Sea if I had not, to my complete surprise, received a letter from Marina two weeks later. Moreover, in this letter, to my pleasant surprise, she did not hide her friendly feelings toward me. I wrote back to her at once, and after that, we continued to communicate by letter and by phone. In a short time, I began to visit her once a month, traveling by train from Kishinev to Odessa. Being a poor student, I lived on a quite limited budget, while Marina's financial status was significantly better than mine. Each time returning from a trip to Odessa, I unexpectedly found money in one of the pockets of my luggage. When it happened the first time, I asked Marina if she had put the money in my luggage, which question my future wife escaped with silence. As the same situation happened many more times, it became obvious that Marina was surreptitiously helping me to make ends meet. I justified accepting her monetary gifts because without them, I would not have had enough money to buy train tickets to Odessa. We enjoyed being together, and after a year of dating, my girlfriend began to visit me in Kishinev, where she stayed with acquaintances of her father.

It was natural that I should be Marina's knight in shining armor, but there were times when she was my protector. Once we went out to the main Kishinev movie theater. Arriving a little early, we were walking near the cinema and stopped on the sidewalk to examine a large poster of a movie that was coming soon. Next to us stood a group of bored young people who did not have anything else to do but bother pedestrians with their rude remarks. While I was standing next to Marina, looking at the poster, two of them started to bully me. I pretended not to hear what was said, but the bullying was gradually increasing. I told Marina to step aside when I tried to respond to the insults. But such was my companion that instead of agreeing to my way of solving the situation peacefully, Marina, like a tigress protecting her cubs, shouted at the offenders with such strength and outrage that they silently turned their backs to us and disappeared into the crowd.

I was so comfortable with our relationship during our student years that for the next two years, like a real fool, I did not officially propose to Marina. Thankfully, she was modest and patient enough not to raise the issue. As I realized later, marriage was indeed important to her, but following the established tradition, she waited for me to take the first step. My penitent excuse for my long procrastination was that our relationship was so nice that I did not think marriage would change anything. This thinking ended when I graduated from medical school in 1964. As education in the Soviet Union was free of charge, in exchange each student was supposed to work as a physician in one of rural villages in the Moldovan Republic. In order to be assigned geographically closer to Marina, who was in her last year of study at the Odessa Meteorological Institute, it was necessary to formalize our relationship. With a joyful laugh, she agreed to my proposal even before

I'd finished getting the words out, and we at once applied for a marriage license and registration. We were married in 1964, when Marina was twenty-one and I was twenty-three. It was a secular, civil marriage in one of Odessa's municipal buildings.

A week later, we traveled to my hometown to introduce Marina to my parents. Despite our great relationship, I did not have any idea how important it was for her to meet my family. We arrived at the railway station and from there went to my house on foot. During our walk, Marina was incredibly excited. She was not walking; she was almost flying and excitedly greeting any stranger we met on the way to my home while radiating happiness and unhidden *joie de vivre*.

The meeting with my parents and my brother's family was wonderful. As I had expected, my parents fell in love with Marina right away, and later she always had a good relationship with each member of my family. When we returned to Odessa, we held a modest wedding ceremony with our families, altogether around twenty-five people. The small number of guests was in reverse proportion to the strength of our marriage.

First Employment Experiences

While Marina continued her last year of study in Odessa, after graduating from medical school, I was assigned to work as a pediatrician in Malaeshti, a large Moldovan village. Though we lived a hundred kilometers from each other, we visited each other once or twice a month, traveling by bus or by hitchhiking. In a year, Marina graduated from her institute, and by the same rule that was applied to me, state authorities assigned her to work in Kishinev, the Moldovan capital. Though we lived separately, we saw each other whenever it was possible. We were young, so a significant distance between us did not prevent us from meeting. Since I was often on duty at the hospital and could not leave work, Marina visited me more often than I visited her. When she arrived at the little apartment where I lived, the first thing she did was to clean it thoroughly. There was not too much to do in the village, there was no TV, so usually we went early to bed. Never again in our lives did we have so many hours of sweet sleep as we did in the village of Malaeshti.

Once when I was walking in the village alone, a local veterinarian demanded that I visit his house in order to examine his allegedly sick daughter. I could not refuse and in the father's car went to examine his daughter. As I'd expected from the previous requests, when we arrived at the veterinarian's house, his daughter was in excellent health. I was ready to leave, but with sly smiles on their faces, the veterinarian and his wife locked the entrance door and invited, or rather ordered me to stay with them for lunch. Nothing was left for me to do but to join the couple's feast. I decided that in a brief time I would pretend to be significantly drunk, which would provide me with an excuse for leaving their odd hospitality. I was ready to drink a third glass of wine when we heard a delicate knock at the door. I prepared myself to use this interruption as an opportunity to escape, when on the threshold, I saw my Marina in all her glory, who had come for a surprise visit. While traveling on the bus to Malaeshti, she had met a farmer from the collective farm, a joker and gossiper, who pretended to know me personally and told Marina that her husband spent his free time with the hospital's nurses. Though the lie spoiled her mood, she did not believe it and stopped talking with the gossiper.

When Marina arrived in Malaeshti, she did not find me at home, but with help of the hospital driver—who knew the whereabouts of everyone in the village—she reached the house where my hosts tried to force me to drink another glass of Moldovan wine. In anticipation of a pleasant surprise, Marina knocked on the door, entered, and found me, her husband, in a drunken state that she'd never seen before. Slightly disoriented and stuttering, I tried to explain her my unseemly appearance. But my wife could not stand the sight of her drunk husband, and still unwittingly, under the influence of the unpleasant remarks from the bus passenger, she sent me a look full of rebuke and displeasure. Refusing to listen to the hosts' entreaties, she resolutely turned on her heels, flung open the door, exited, and slammed it, leaving me alone with my too-hospitable hosts.

Very soon after Marina's departure, to my relief, the couple decided the party was over. Still in a state of intoxication, I got home within an hour and knocked on the door of my apartment. Without taking her rebuking eyes off me, Marina silently opened the door. Being almost sober by this time, I explained to her what had happened. Her anger quickly dissipated, and being fully forgiven, in relief, I went to bed for a good sleep. Past episode proved to me that she was quickly able to forget and forgive unpleasant things, which was so important in our future uncomplicated and harmonious matrimonial life.

During my stay in that village, there was another touching episode. This time it reminded me of O. Henry's story "The Gift of the Magi." In the story, the heroine, Della, for Christmas gift cuts and sells her beautiful hair in order to buy Jim, her beloved husband, a chain for his watch, while Jim sells his watch to buy Della combs for her long hair. In our version of the story, we wanted to surprise each other too. I wanted to arrive unexpectedly in Korneshti, the village where she worked on an anti-hail expedition, while in turn, she wanted to surprise me by going to the village where I worked. As a result, each of us ended up in the other's location. When Marina got to my village, she learned that I had left in the morning to meet her at her place. As happened often, the telephone was not functioning that day, and mobile phones were awaiting to be invented. Marina was quite upset. To calm down, she traveled not to her village but to the city of Kishinev, where our good friends lived at the time. Many years later, these friends laughed when they recalled how they persuaded a frustrated and tired Marina to take a bath and how she was crying there after the funny confusion.

Three years after our marriage, in 1967, Marina and I were able to reunite in the city of Odessa. My first job in Odessa was as a pediatrician, while she found a job as a scientist-researcher in Odessa's Maritime Academy. On our days off, we enjoyed going for long walks, and in the summertime, we went swimming in the Black Sea. Ever since early childhood, reading had always been Marina's favorite form of leisure, and it still was. A typical bookworm, she swallowed one book after another. When I asked how she was able to read an average-sized book in two or three days, she explained that she knew how to skip secondary details. However, when I later read the same book myself and asked her about these secondary details, she always surprised me with her knowledge of the small particulars of the book's contents.

Watching her as she read, I could not help but notice how beautiful she was, and I could not understand why other people did not see her beauty as well. She had an oval face with smooth and glowing skin, and her head was adorned by slightly curly brown hair. Her almond-shaped, dark-brown eyes had a gentle, warm, and compassionate appearance. Her eyebrows were thick, black, and, like mine, slightly fused at the nasal bridge. I told her many times that she was beautiful and attractive, but in response to my compliments, she only smiled back mysteriously, with a look that let me know she did not take me seriously.

After we reunited, we lived with Marina's mother and stepfather in a communal apartment. Sofía Lvovna, Marina's mother, never hid her disdain toward me. She perceived herself as a highly cultured woman from the celebrated, respected, and famous city of Odessa. Physicians in the Soviet Union, unlike physicians in the West, earned ridiculously small salaries (until now they do). The main reason for her openly disrespectful attitude toward me was that she thought her daughter could find a more attractive prospect than a physician from a provincial town. Between her and me, there were never obvious conflicts, mostly because when she tried to start an argument, I responded with a deep silence, a powerful device that barred her from opening the gates of a quarrel. I was firmly convinced that it was a waste of time to figure out who was right and who was wrong in trivial matters, so why spend our fast-flowing lives dealing with such trifling things? Losing me as a potential passionate opponent in the argument, my mother-in-law eventually brought her complaints to Marina and tried to involve her daughter in the conflict. These attempts were doomed to fail, since from the time we met, Marina did not doubt my decency. After Marina's resentful reactions, Sophia Lvovna, in an offended voice, always made the same declaration. "For your Vovka, you are ready to chop off the head of anyone who says something negative about him."

I never took Marina's love and devotion for granted and tried to pay her back in the same coin.

Marriage As a Creative Undertaking

Once, when we had reunited in Odessa, my wife gave me a lesson on how, in her opinion, the relationship between husband and wife should be and here how it happened. I loved music and soon found people in the city who shared the same interest. After the establishment of the socialist regime, in the Soviet Union there existed a strong censorship that dictated "proletarian" culture, music included. For example, young people were supposed to listen only to the songs of "social realism." Social realism simply meant that the entire Soviet culture was supposed to be presented in such a way that it reflected the ideological platform of the Communist Party. As a result, during Soviet times, the overwhelming number of songs, including songs about love and romance, were supposed to have a subliminal political indoctrination. The strict cultural environment of control softened after Stalin's death, and already in the 1960s, there was a well-established by people underground way of listening to foreign music. This music consisted mostly of Western songs and melodies recorded mostly from records and tapes that were brought home by sailors and diplomats returning from overseas travel. These pieces of music were recorded on reel-to-reel tape recorders, which at that time had just appeared in the Soviet Union.

Recordings of Ray Conniff, Paul Mauriat, Annunzio Mantovani, and Gianni Morandi, with their orchestras, and singers such as Engelbert Humperdinck, Tom Jones, Edith Piaf, Frank Sinatra, Matt Monroe, and many other performers were recorded and rerecorded many times until the reproduction was totally distorted. A significant part of these recordings was also the Soviet semiunderground performers such as Vladimir Visotsky, Bulat Okujawa, and Alexander Galich. Those who wanted to hear the protest songs of those performers, some of which did not agree with the official ideology of the Communist Party, listened to them on tape recorders. The Communist Party was not taking measures against this type of underground music because sprinkled in the recordings were also many patriotic songs devoted to the heroism of the Soviet people during the Second World War. In my opinion, nonconformist lyrics from their repertoire with the primacy of individual versus collective played an important role in the eventual fall of the Soviet Union.

Underground music was popularized by numerous individuals who had quality tape recorders and access to firsthand soundtracks of popular songs. Owners of good recordings of the well-liked foreign performers were popular among the young people who wanted to have high-quality recordings.

Once, when I was making house calls as a pediatrician, I was ready to leave my young patient, when his father, obviously satisfied with my services, suggested that I listen to his first-class recordings of Beatles, Nat King Cole, and Paul Anka. I enjoyed music of this type, which was officially forbidden to Soviet citizens. I was so impressed by the excellent music recordings that, for a while, I forgot that I must continue to make my house call rounds. As for my host, he was so pleased with my appreciation of his collection that he suggested I visit him again for another listening experience. Moreover, to my further satisfaction, this lover of music told me I could come with my own reel-to-reel tape, and he would record for me an entire reel of music of my choice. That made me incredibly happy; I would have my own music collection, which I would then be able to share with my friends.

When I came home, the first thing I did was share the good news with Marina, who, for some unknown reason, did not greet my news with enthusiasm. She did not comment and not saying a word, she went about her own business.

In a week, ready to visit my new friend, I put my Dnepr brand tape recorder, and its tape reels in a backpack. Ready to leave, I said goodbye to my wife. To my surprise, she did not answer me but continued with her household duties. Not understanding what was going on, I paused in my departure and asked her the reason for her unusual reaction. The conversation that followed allowed me to learn more about my wife's perspective on how a marriage should be conducted.

"So, you are going to your new friend to tape music that you like. And what should I do? To remain here while you are going to enjoy your own thing," she said softly. "Go and have a fun time. I will not hold you back. I have other things to do, and I am not as big a music lover as you are. All week we worked and did not see each other, and now on our weekend, we will be separated again. I realize you are a free person, so you can go wherever you want. Go. Goodbye."

Two opposing feelings fought in my chest. On the one hand, it seemed to me that in marriage, though the spouses are together, they are free to be occupied with activities that they like. In other words, it meant Marina was encroaching on my freedom. After four years of marriage, she knew how I liked music. What was wrong if I brought home beautiful music that we would enjoy together? Besides, she already knew that my friend was waiting for me. It seemed to me that her behavior was not fair, that it was a whim.

However . . . however, I was glad that my wife, this precious human being for me, liked being in my company. After all, we did many things separately according to our interests, and if this time she wanted me to be with her then why not? Most times she did not protest my outside interests, but this time she was against one. It was not a big sacrifice to give in to her. From this time, I decided that one of love definitions could be as invisible and powerful energy field that connects two individuals forever. A litmus test for the authenticity of love is an instinctive feeling that each of the spouses cannot exist without the other. We human beings are born and die as separate individuals, and love is the invisible glue that unites and keeps the partners in love together. If people love each other, they must yield to each other.

In the end, I realized that although I missed the arranged music recording session, in yielding to Marina's desire, I helped strengthening our married life for many years in the future. I fully understood that spending time with family, especially when my wife asked for it, was much more important than having a recording of pleasant music. There are many ways to live together, and I chose the one where we share time in pursuit of common interests. That by no means excluded time to pursue our own business. However, spending time together with a person who loves you means intertwining souls on a spiritual level in the flow of time. I understood that while having time to enjoy our individual responsibilities and hobbies, people who are married or are in a close relationship should also find time for mutual spiritual bonding.

Countless songs and poems tell us that one of the main satisfactions in our lives is the realization that for the present and the future, there is another human being who appreciates us as an integral part of their life. If my wife considered me to be her chosen husband then I should consider myself a lucky man because for somebody in this world, I am special and important. Real love is a two-way road where both spouses take and give in equal proportion. I always treasured Marina's affection toward me and invented many things to keep the fire going.

Maybe the divorce between Marina's parents, when she was thirteen, was the reason that she strove for such tight human relationships. She loved life and she loved people.

Addition to the Family

Our son, Alexander, whom we called Sasha, was born in 1967, when Marina was twenty-four. Like any other child in the Soviet Union, he was delivered in one of the freestanding maternity hospitals. The standard hospital stay for the mother and her healthy newborn was seven days then. The universal policy in these maternal hospitals was not to allow members of the family to see the mother and the newborn until they were discharged to go home. Officially, the policy was to prevent infections in the maternal hospitals, though it ignored the chance that the patients themselves could get infected in the hospital during such a prolonged stay. While the mother and the baby were in the maternal hospital, communication with outsiders was carried on in an awkward but familiar scene: family members stood outside, next to the building, while the new mother with her newborn stood inside at one of the windows facing them. The people outside, screaming loudly and energetically gesticulating, exchanged their daily news with the new mothers.

Luckily, I was an exception to this routine. Being a district pediatrician who would soon be taking care of the newborns born in my area of service, I had free access to any maternity hospital in the city. Early in the morning, after a sleepless night, I called my service's dispatcher and learned that before my office hours started in the clinic, I had fifteen house calls to make. On the way to my house calls, I stopped at the maternity hospital where Marina, ready to deliver our baby, had been admitted the previous night. On the porch at the main entrance to the hospital stood a small group of relatives waiting to receive information about their loved ones. At 8:30 a.m., the main door of the building opened, and a nurse's aide appeared on the porch. From the sheet of paper she held in her hand, she solemnly began to read the names of babies born the previous night. In this way, I learned that my son had been born. While the group was dispersing, I announced to the nurse that I was not only the father of a newborn but also a district pediatrician and therefore had free access to the maternity hospital.

Without delay I was allowed to enter, and twenty minutes later came the unforgettable moment when, for the first time, I saw my own newborn son, Alexander, when he was only three hours old. After admiring him and finishing a brief examination, I put him in a cloth diaper and covered him with a blanket, while happiness was filling my heart to the brim. After that, trying to see my wife, I tried entering the part of the maternity hospital where were located patients' rooms but was stopped right away by orderlies and nurses loudly instructing me that it was "*verboten*" for me to enter there. There was no way to persuade the angry chorus. Still, nothing could spoil my celebratory mood after the birth of my son. I apologized and was on my way out to start the house calls in my district when one of the nurses grabbed me by my sleeve.

"Wait, doctor," she said, looking at me. Unexpectedly, the expression on her face was sweet and pleasant. "Before you leave, I have to tell you something special."

"Why do you say that?" I asked.

"You see, I was in the delivery room when your wife was giving birth to your son. She surprised not only me since she was one of those rare women who did not moan or scream during the entire childbirth. On the contrary, between contractions she smiled like she was going through a pleasant experience. Amazing!"

"Maybe that's because she really wanted to have our child," I assumed, proud for Marina.

"Practically, every woman wants to have her child. There is nothing unusual in it," the nurse objected. "But to smile during labor—that is something I've hardly ever seen before."

For the rest of the day, I made house calls, running from one floor to another in different buildings, and later I saw patients in the clinic. It was dark outside when, after a busy working day, I could return to the maternity hospital. On the way, I hurriedly managed to buy Marina not only a box of chocolates but, most important to me then, a bouquet of flowers. Buying flowers in the middle of winter was not an easy undertaking in Odessa. I gave my presents to an orderly, who promised to deliver them to Marina. On the following days, I brought similar presents to my hospitalized wife, but being busy at work, I did not have time to see her during the daytime.

In seven days, exactly as medical regulations required, our son, a newcomer to the world, and his mother were discharged from the hospital. On this joyful day on the way to our communal apartment, as a newly fledged father, I was holding my son in my arms, while Marina was walking next to me. Suddenly, her face assumed a serious expression.

"Listen, Vovka," she said in an unfamiliar didactic and instructive tone, "where was your head when I was in the maternal hospital? What was the problem with you? I was sick and tired of your daily presents of flowers and chocolates. Are you so naïve as not to know that the food in hospitals is inedible? Did you expect me to keep eating nothing but chocolate while admiring your flowers? I would have been hungry every day if not for my mother, and even she barely brought me enough food to eat."

I was ready to apologize for my outrageously poorly informed behavior, but Marina did not let me open my mouth.

"I know that you did not do it intentionally," she, who hardly ever complained, said. "Even more, I am upset that for all the time I was in the hospital, all the rooms there were occupied, so I was forced to have a bed in the hospital's drafty corridor. I am surprised I did not catch cold there."

I could not have done anything about removing her from the drafty corridor, but how guilty did I feel for not providing my Marina with food! Who would have thought that conditions in the hospital could be so appalling?

In the Soviet Union, paid maternity leave lasted for at least two months. During this time, Marina took care of our son while I was busy working two, and sometimes three, jobs to make ends meet. In my free time, I did my best to help my wife. Because we were still having chronic financial difficulties, Marina started looking for work. Fortunately, she had a good resume from her earlier work experience and soon found a job as a scientist in a thermodynamic faculty at Odessa Higher Engineering Marine School. During the first month after the birth of our son, she worked part-time. With her meteorological background, she got a quick promotion. Meanwhile, we were looking for help to take care of our son, but all we could find, with great difficulty, was a semiliterate woman.

Marina was a good mother. Taking care of our child was her main responsibility. We decided to take turns caring for our son when he woke us up, but no matter whose turn it was, she was the first to jump from the bed to pacify our crying baby.

Soon after his birth, we realized that he could not tolerate either cow's milk or Marina's breast milk. In the Soviet Union in 1967, baby formula was still an unknown commodity, though it had been introduced in the West a whole century earlier, in 1865. The only way to feed a child at that time was either with breast milk or a cow's milk, whole or diluted. Our son refused to eat everything we were trying to give him, and like other parents in the country, we went through tough times trying to make our son consume at least small amounts of the offered food. Discomfort related to food and abdominal pain was waking him up in the middle of the night, resulting in many sleepless and exhausting nights for Marina and me.

When Sasha was three months old, we bought him a rocking cradle. After that, when I woke up in the middle of the night, I could often see Marina in the darkness of the room. To help our son fall asleep, sitting next to his cradle with her eyes closed--I did not know whether she was sleeping at that time or not --she rocked his crib, rhythmically pressing on one of the rocking runners with her foot.

Being a pediatrician and trying to be a good father, I did my best to follow the common belief that a doctor should not treat members of his own family. Desperately trying to help our son, we were bringing him for consultations with different local medical luminaries, many times receiving conflicting advice. If some of them agreed to a possibility that our son had allergy to cow's milk, they all as one disagreed about a possibility of an allergy to mother's milk. On the contrary, they insisted that Marina must continue breastfeeding her baby. Regarding complaints about our child's poor sleep, all of them maintained that we should not spoil him by giving in to his whims and strongly recommended not to pacify him when he was crying. Marina and I were taking this advice with a grain of salt and not implementing it in life, but eventually, after many sleepless nights, we decided to try to see what would happen if we ignored our son's crying in the middle of the night. Our decision was disastrous. At five o'clock in the morning, after hours of crying, our son's voice had changed from sonorous to hoarse. With a guilty feeling that we were abusing our poor child, Marina picked up our Sasha and lulled him to pacify him. He fell asleep in moments, with his little head on his mother's shoulder.

When Sasha reached five months of age, his food allergies became even worse. Both Marina and I felt tremendously frustrated at the futility of our efforts to find food that would agree with him. Every day he became thinner. At six months of age, Sasha began to suffer from diarrhea due to a deficiency in his nutrition. His gradual deterioration continued, and with the diagnosis of a nutritional problem, he was admitted to the hospital where I worked at that time. While in hospital, his condition continued to deteriorate. Not being able to help our poor son, Marina and I lived in daily emotional stress, which paralyzed us. On the fourth day of hospitalization, Sasha's condition was very bad. He developed a high fever, and his breathing became fast and forceful. He was fighting for his life.

During the morning rounds, our doctor told us that to save our child, we needed to obtain Sigmamycin, a foreign-produced antibiotic. After begging, cajoling, and feeling humiliated during a visit to the bureaucrat who was responsible for the distribution of this antibiotic, eventually I obtained the medication. Entering the hospital room where my son was, I found Marina sitting next to his bed, holding a cold compress on Sasha's forehead. She did not cry, and she did not answer my greeting. She was completely concentrated on taking care of our son. Unconsciously, she was blocking her thoughts about a possible outcome of his condition. Instead, she focused on what was happening at the moment.

I left the room and went to the nurse, handed her the ten-day supply of the medication I'd brought and a short time later, our son received the first dose of antibiotic. Right after that, the nurse tried to restart his IV fluid infusion. Alas, due to many earlier unsuccessful venipuncture attempts, his veins were inaccessible. Eventually, on the doctor's order, instead of an IV, a needle was inserted into the inner surface of Sasha's upper thigh. Though this ancient method of rehydration had a sophisticated name, hypodermoclysis, it was barely effective, since the infused fluids were absorbed very slowly from that place, and eventually these fluids produced an ugly swelling.

Marina and I did not sleep during the following night at all, but in the following morning, we were not tired at all as Sasha's condition had miraculously improved. His temperature had gone down, and his respiratory rate had slowed to normal. We perked up even more at noon when he opened his eyes wide and with interest looked at what was going around him. His suffering expression was gone. With tears in her eyes, Marina tenderly kissed his face many times and then rewarded me with her happy smile as well.

Doctors Are Not Always Right

Three days later, Sasha's pneumonia was under control, but he continued to have symptoms of intolerance to cow's milk. By this time, Marina's breast milk had completely dried.

In our earlier years in Kishinev, Marina and I, at different times, had rented a small room in an apartment that belonged to a wonderful older couple. We addressed them in the Russian manner as Aunt Leah and Uncle Arkady. They became our dear older friends, and when they learned that our son was in the hospital, to help us, these couple took a train and came from Kishinev to Odessa. In anticipation of their arrival, we did not know that their visit will result in an incredibly successful result.

When we met, Aunt Leah listened attentively to what Marina was telling her about our son's nutritional problems and after Marina finished, to our surprise, with a maternal smile, Aunt Leah confidently said, "While you might not believe me, and although I am not a doctor, I will help your son."

"I am surprised that all your doctors do not know what to do in this case," she continued with a warm expression on her face. "Just wait and see what I am going to bring to your son tomorrow. You do not have a problem anymore, kids."

The next morning, the old couple came to the hospital with a vegetable soup that consisted mainly of millet cereal. I was sure that if the pediatric luminaries saw this soup intended as food for a six-month-old baby, they might faint. Nevertheless, to our amazement our son, who for many weeks had refused food, as if by magic, became a voracious eater from the moment he tried it. Excited, we watched him with our eyes widely open as he greedily sucked the soup from the bottle with a hearty appetite. The feeding problem was resolved as if it had never existed, and Marina glowed with joy. I realized that if not for our wonderful older Kishinev friends, the miracle would not have happened. That precious life lesson taught us that besides valuable scientific methods of medicine, there are also plenty effective treatment methods of traditional folk medicine.

Guarding the Child

The hospital administration was kind enough to provide my family with a hospital room intended for VIP patients. Our isolated private room was located on the first floor, and its windows were facing the front of the hospital, where the drivers of the hospital vehicles often congregated when they were between runs. They would talk and laugh loudly, sometimes waking up our son, who at this time was recovering from his serious illness. Marina, a devoted and caring young mother, was not shy about coming to terms with such a nuisance. When the noise outside would reach a high level, Marina, her son's keeper, took active steps.

"Dear drivers, can I ask you to lower your voice? I am sorry, but recently my son was very sick, and the noise is waking him up," she said apologetically but with a tone of determination. The drivers, surprised by such an unusual demand, were speechless for a minute, smiled and then followed Marina's request. For years afterward, hospital drivers teased me, reminding me of my wife, a devoted lioness, who did not hesitate to appeal to them to not bother her son.

A New Profession

After our son's full recovery, Marina was again able to work full-time. Her natural aptitude in mathematics helped her to quickly meet the requirements of her new profession as a research physicist. Then and later, I could not help but be amazed at how capable she was at mastering her new career. She was born with an intuitive ability to meet the challenges of understanding new concepts. To me, who took the requirements of study seriously, Marina's attitude was strange. For me, the process of learning, especially in a profession that provided a livelihood for the family, was a serious challenge, but Marina was mastering her new profession without stress or excitement. For her, the most important part of life was all about her family. For example, while she was still studying at the Meteorological Institute, when I asked her how her studies were going, she refused to discuss it, telling me that the subject was boring and not interesting.

Once, back during our student years, by coincidence we both had a test on subject of Marxism–Leninism at the same time in our respective teaching institutions. Using this unique opportunity, we agreed to prepare for the test together. So, I arrived from Kishinev to Odessa with my luggage full of books on the subject. The day after my arrival, when I joined Marina and her good friend to prepare for the test, from the very beginning, I understood that her attitude was totally incompatible with my way of studying. Though none of us believed in delusional--as it appeared to me--Marx and Lenin's doctrines, I nevertheless took preparation for the test seriously, while Marina and her friend often interrupted our study with extraneous conversations. While I liked to study for long stretches of time, my partners did not miss an opportunity to take breaks from work. I usually studied until nine o'clock in the evening, but Marina and her friend studied only until six o'clock in the evening. On the second study day, to our mutual satisfaction, each of us went our own way. I resumed preparation for the test in the district library, while my recent companions continued to enjoy their preparation for the test in Marina's apartment. In a couple of weeks, we got results of the exam. I was quite upset that Marina, who had taken a lot less time and dedication to prepare for the exams, got a higher grade than me.

By the same token, when Marina started working as a physicist, she was not eager to share details about her scientific work with me. Instead, she liked to discuss news related to our cultural life, our family, and the community where we lived. She liked to tell me about the books she read and movies that she had seen.

Cholera in Odessa

In 1970, a cholera epidemic broke out in Odessa. The main source of the disease was seawater contaminated with sewage on Odessa's famous beaches. From the pre-Revolutionary sewer pipes, the city's sewage flowed straight without any treatment straight to the Black Sea. A strict quarantine was declared in the city. At that time, I worked in the infectious disease hospital, and the administration commandeered me and one more physician to take care of the cholera-stricken patients. Afraid of getting the illness, most of the hospital physicians refused to work with cholera patients. As I recall, in the span of five days, my colleague and I admitted one hundred forty-six severely dehydrated patients, of whom fourteen died at the hospital. The perimeter of each district was under guard by KGB soldiers, and not a single worker, doctor, nurse, or orderly was allowed to leave their assigned unit until the end of the epidemic. Day after day, admitting patients, my colleague and I did not sleep for the first five days of the epidemic. Because of the strict quarantine rules, the employees who worked with the cholera patients were allowed to communicate with their relatives and friends by standing on each side of a stone wall that was guarded by KGB soldiers. People on both sides of the wall were concerned and worried. Marina did not miss a single day of coming to visit me. She came together with our three-year-old son, and standing on different sides of the wall, we exchanged our news. Seeing Marina and our son was a daily celebration during the tragic time.

Everyday Life and the Soviet Ideology

Though Marina was a scientist, and I was a physician, and we both were working full-time, living from paycheck to paycheck, our salaries were barely enough to support our family's needs. We were still living in one large room of a communal apartment where we shared a kitchen, a restroom, and a corridor with three other families. Ever since I was a child, I have loved the people from my country, but I hated the communist system where the state controlled everything and where an individual was considered as an easily replaceable commodity in the name of the collective needs. Among ourselves we said that, as in other communist countries, the Russian socialist system did not allow people to live and did not allow them to die.

When Marina and I met, she was an apolitical person. Most of her leisure time she devoted to reading, and she hardly ever read newspapers or listened to the radio. She lived in her own world, and the reality of our communist society was barely of interest to her. After we met, I did my best to open her eyes to the hypocrisy of the Soviet system, a system where the propaganda machine daily indoctrinated the minds of its citizens, successfully producing imaginary rosy pictures of the society that was in decay. In the Soviet Union, where the uncontested government had the unlimited power of coercion, those dissidents who were immune to communist propaganda were easily neutralized and controlled in a thousand and one ways by the state. To me, as to an ethnic Jew, state-cultivated and state-supported anti-Semitism was repugnant, and shocking.

Gradually, listening to my and our friends' arguments, Marina gained a clearer idea of what was happening in the country, eventually breaking the cocoon of ignorance of the real truth of the "unique communist experiment," where anybody who disagreed with the system was considered to be a dangerous foreign element.

Time to Go West

The cholera epidemic in Odessa in August 1970, when I had the opportunity to witness the utter backwardness of the Soviet medical system, was an important event that motivated my eventual decision to leave the country where many generations of my family had lived. The other factor was government-supported anti-Semitism. A few months after the end of the epidemic, as an active participant in the fight against cholera, I was sent by the hospital's administration to the Kiev Institute for Advanced Medical Studies with the goal of preparing me to be an expert in the treatment of "Especially Dangerous" infectious diseases.

It did not take long time for me to realize that at the Kiev Institute, they taught only the common facts, which I knew well without them. Having plenty of free time and wanting to spend it purposefully, I began to study homeopathic medicine. After returning to Odessa, I continued to visit Kiev, where I attended monthly seminars on homeopathy. On one of those monthly trips to Kiev from Odessa, a doctor I knew from the past entered my train compartment. From him, I learned that together with his family he was on the way from the Soviet Union to the West. He enlightened me in detail on how to safely apply for permission to leave the Soviet Union for good. When I came home from Kiev, I impatiently rang the doorbell to my three-family communal apartment. My wife opened the door, giving me her charming, warm smile.

"Marina, we are going to leave the Soviet Union," were my first words. "It looks like the authorities have opened the Iron Curtain just high enough for us to escape the country. During my trip to Kiev, I met people on their way to the West, and they explained to me how it can be done. Imagine, if it all works out, in several months, our family will become free people in the free world. Do you agree with my plan to escape to freedom?"

Marina looked at me intently with her beautiful brown eyes, where I could read a shade of light rebuke. "I cannot believe you, Vovka. What are you talking about? What answer do you expect from me, you silly one?" she said with an angelic smile on her face. And then, as if she were Ruth from the Bible, she said, "Wherever you go, I will go. I am ready whenever you are."

"Aren't you afraid?" I asked. "We don't know even if Russian authorities will allow us to leave anytime soon, and we don't know what will happen to us when we find ourselves abroad."

"Don't you worry, Vovka. The main thing is that we love each other. The rest is just a footnote. In any case, it will not be worse than being in our decaying communist trap."

In August 1974, accompanied with my devoted partner and our seven-year-old son, Sasha, we crossed the border to the West and found ourselves in beautiful Vienna, Austria.

Italy for $150

Spending a week in Vienna, we moved on to the friendly and beautiful Italy. In Italy we lived in Rome on Napoleon III Street. Our hostess was signora Maraviglia, who rented the entire fifth floor of the large apartment house to Russian emigrants. We "had privilege" to live in one of her fifteen rooms on the floor. We were lucky to have a separate room, which signora Maraviglia allowed us to have in respect to my *"seignior doctore"* profession.

In another two months, we would be leaving for Chicago, which was to become the final destination on our long journey from the country of so-called proletarian dictatorship to the country of true democracy and freedom. But before we left Europe, we went on a ten-day trip to Northern Italy. This trip was possible thanks to Marina.

"Listen, Vovka," she said to me one day after we had already spent several weeks waiting in expectation of our visas to the USA. "Who knows if we'll ever have a chance to return to this magnificent country. After all, we don't have any idea how life will turn out for us in America. At best, we will return to our professions. But it might end up that you will become something like a janitor, and I, with my primitive knowledge of English, could become a cleaning lady. In any case, our main objective is to give our son a good education, so what profession we are going to be in does not matter. Meanwhile, with two hundred fifty dollars left, we can spend one hundred fifty dollars of it for a week of travel in Italy, as long as we are already here."

I expressed my doubt. "How it is possible that for a hundred fifty dollars all of us can travel this country for an entire week?"

"Don't worry, Vovchik, I've thought of everything," Marina said, exposing in a charming smile her snow-white teeth. "I've been to the railway station and learned that we can buy cheap Eurail Passes for each of us. Just imagine, this pass will allow both of us to travel twenty thousand kilometers in Italy, and our seven-year-old son will travel for free," she finished triumphantly.

If not for her initiative, we would not have had that unforgettable journey through Northern Italy. We visited Florence, Bologna, Venice, Milan, Pisa, and Genoa. To master such an itinerary, we obeyed our timetable with strict discipline. In charge of our family group was Marina, our main inspirer and, if necessary, our wise disciplinarian. Wherever we were, we slept in the cheapest lodging we could find. To leave to the next city, at six o'clock in the morning, we were already at the railroad station. On the way, we ate sandwiches prepared by Marina in advance. At each new destination, we spent a day or two, then traveled to the next beautiful Italian city.

Even counting every Italian lira, when we bought food, we were never hungry. While saving every penny, passing numerous Italian pubs, I felt jealous to see carefree visitors with relaxed expressions on their faces gathered in front of them, sipping beer or wine—luxuries totally beyond our budget. That's why when we arrived at New York Airport, the first things I did was I bought a bottle of beer and drank it in one gulp.

In Florence, passing a trattoria, on its window, we saw a notice advertising a beef dish for an incredibly low price. Ever since arriving in Italy, we had not been able to afford meat; however, now we decided that our son should have it. Marina and I were happy to see how Sasha enjoyed his delicious meal, but after he finished eating and we received the check, it came time for reckoning. Not expecting our bill to be as high, we questioned the waiter. From him, we learned that the cheap price we'd seen on the sign on the window of the restaurant was the price not for the entire dish, but for one hundred grams of beef. Not having any experience with such a commercial way of advertising, we had ordered a generous portion of meat for our son. There was nothing else to do but to pay the bill.

Being in austerity mode, how happy were we when on one rainy day our son found a cheap umbrella that had been lost by someone on the bank of a Venetian canal. Another cause for joy was a working cigarette lighter that I found next to the famous Milan cathedral. When one is short of money any useful thing becomes precious.

After we got back to Rome, we were finally given our long-awaited visas to America. Filled with excitement and apprehension, we soon boarded a plane for the USA.

We—Americans; $3.75 Per Hour

"Roman Holidays" lasted two months and at the end of them, in October 1974, we found ourselves in the city of Chicago, the final destination of our long journey from the country of the dictatorship of the proletariat to the country of democracy and freedom. When we arrived in Chicago, I had the feeling that we had landed on another planet, and this feeling does not leave me almost fifty years later.

It was the Jewish Federation of Chicago that helped us to settle, providing us with a temporary place to live and with a monthly stipend until I could pass the tests to be certified as a physician and find work. For our monthly living expenses, we received $174. Using this money only for essentials, we managed to make ends meet, being happy to live in the country of freedom.

While I spent most of the time preparing for my medical exams, Marina became our breadwinner. Despite her limited knowledge of English language, she found her first job as a filing clerk in a large insurance company. She was paid $3.75 per hour, and even that small addition to our budget improved our financial situation right away. In a month, we moved to a project building at Clarendon and Wilson in Chicago. It was the first time in our lives that we lived in a two-bedroom apartment that we did not have to share with anybody. We had enough money for food, and in our apartment, we had heat, hot and cold running water, a gas stove, and a refrigerator. We both agreed that for just such luxuries alone, it had been well worth moving to America.

On our arrival to Chicago from the Soviet Union in October 1974, the Jewish Federation of Chicago helped us to get temporary quarters at the Pratt Hotel in East Rogers Park. After we arrived, we soon became a part of a group of our newfound close friends. Though they were of different professions and lived in different places, all of them were immigrants from the Soviet Union. It was natural among us to address each other by first name. Only Marina was usually addressed not by her first name but by the nickname "Mom." This name she deserved because of the indelible part of her personality being sincerely concerned about the health and well-being of our friends, always helping them to deal with the challenges of life.

Back to School; Encounter with Spirituality

October was the second month of the school year, so we placed our seven-year-old son in the nearby public school. He studied there for not more than three weeks and then refused to go back to school. The main problem for him was that as a recent immigrant, he had limited knowledge of the English language. The schoolchildren mercilessly bullied him both verbally and physically, not willing to forgive him for his inability to communicate in English. Being the first immigrant from Russia at the school, he could not expect support from students who spoke the same language as he did. Having our own struggles with the English language, Marina and I were skeptical that a conversation with school officials would be constructive, especially since Sasha's confrontations mostly took place outside the school walls. We felt there was no other choice than to look for another school for him without delay. At that time, Jewish organizations were pairing recent immigrants with volunteer American Jewish sponsors. Our voluntary sponsors were American citizens Lilly and Eric Baum. Sixty years old Lilly Baum was active in helping Jewish refuseniks—those who were not allowed by authorities to leave the Soviet Union. She was also highly active in helping Russian immigrants settle in their new country. It was she who was instrumental in helping us find a good school for our son, a school which he successfully attended for the next seven years. Thanks to Lilly Baum's efforts, Sasha soon became a second-year pupil in Chicago's uptown Anshe Emet Day School. There, he was the first Jewish Russian immigrant student at a Grammar School, and from the first day, his teachers treated him well. Naturally, his poor knowledge of the English language presented him with many unpredictable challenges. Since I was home preparing for my medical recertification test, while Marina was working at minimum-wage jobs, the school's administration was kind enough at first to allow us to pay half of the normal yearly school fee.

The Anshe Emet Day School belonged to the conservative movement in Jewish America. Both Marina and I had grown up in a society where religion was forbidden and persecuted in different ways, while a zealous atheism--in my opinion, nothing more than another type of faith--replaced other religions. My parents and Marina's parents were ethnically Jewish, but they did not believe in God and did not practice religion.

At the time Marina and I met, thoughts of religion were far from her mind. As for me, despite not having any exposure to organized religion in my younger years, I had then and now a strong intuitive belief in God's existence. I was also exposed to thoughts about the idea of God from uncensored works by writers like Tolstoy, Dostoevsky, Gorky, Dickens, and Chesterton, in whose books many religious ideas were presented. In view of the utter mystery of universe and of hidden complexity of all that surrounds us, I believed in God on a personal level, but I never met face-to-face with anyone in my childhood with whom I could share my religious views. Without using the concept of God, I still cannot find any other way of explaining the mysteriously simple but infinitely complicated world in which I am a temporary guest.

When our son became a student in the religious primary school, I was working long hours as a pediatric resident. For different reasons, I hardly ever attended a synagogue in the Soviet Union.

It never crossed my mind to attend the synagogue to which Sasha's religious school belonged. But the opposite happened with Marina. On her own, and without clearly expressing her own ideas of religion, she began to attend Shabbat religious services, which took place in the synagogue that was at the same building as Sasha's school. When I asked her the reason for this decision, she answered that she felt compelled to set a good example for our son. However, as time passed, Marina attended religious services regardless of our son's schedule. Soon I realized that the moving force behind her going to religious services was a conscious decision to include faith in God in her value system and maybe to be a role model for our son.

First Entertainment. Marina's Further Success in Her Working Career

Soon after arriving in Chicago, we discovered something we had not known existed—garage sales. Thanks to the possibility of obtaining used but essential things for cheap prices at garage sales, among other items, we bought an armchair and a black-and-white TV. By that time, in 1974, transistor TVs had almost completely replaced the tube variety. The tube TV we bought at a garage sale hardly showed a picture, but I was able to fix it by replacing some of the tubes. The old TV's picture quality then became excellent, and it was the main source of our entertainment during family time.

The next great news was when Marina found a much better paying position as an EKG technician at one of the hospitals in the north of Chicago. Before she went for her first work interview there, using my earlier limited experience, I had taught her what I could about the EKG. During the interview, Marina had the chutzpah to say that she had worked as an EKG technician in the Soviet Union. It was a lie, justified only because it was difficult to live in poverty. In any case, the chief of the EKG department at once recognized that Marina knew almost nothing about EKG technology. Yet he did not hide that he was impressed with her genuine certificates and diplomas and even more by her prepossessing personality.

"Okay, I know you don't have a clue about EKG technology," he said, summarizing the interview. "However, I have not been able to fill this position for more than a month, and I see you are a pleasant woman with a good education. Also, I like how you blush sweetly when you fib. I am myself a recent immigrant from Poland, so I know how desperately you need this job. Go to the human resources office and tell them that you are hired with a probation period of one month."

Marina was in seventh heaven. We celebrated as a family at a local McDonald's restaurant, a treat we had not been able to afford until that day. Leaving our apartment to go to the restaurant, while I was locking the door, I noticed, at the end of the corridor, a maintenance worker from our project building who was looking intently at me while I was locking the door.

To our distress, when we got home from McDonald's, we saw that our apartment had been robbed. We did not have anything valuable in our apartment, but all of us, especially our son, missed our black-and-white TV refurbished by me. Not Marina. She was not one to easily give up. "Hey, don't be upset," she told Sasha and me with an upbeat smile. "I did not tell you, but each month I have saved a little money. I am going to give you all what I saved, and you go and buy another TV. This time, instead of a black-and-white TV, we will buy a color TV because we are winners, not losers. The other day I was passing a TV repair shop and saw there a used color set at a reasonable price."

In two hours, in our apartment stood every immigrant's dream—a color television, the first in our lives. It was not new, it had a rainbow distortion on the left and top-right corners of the screen, and the picture was not ideal, but who cared? We had a color TV, which we could never have afforded before.

For several months, Marina continued to enjoy her work as an EKG technician. Thanks to her natural ability to grasp everything on the fly, in a remarkably short time, she made stunning strides in conversational English. My written English, which I had studied at school and on my own in Russia, was much better than hers, but Marina was not only better at conversational English, she was also much better at pronouncing words in English than I was.

It is not for nothing that wise people say everything around us is temporary. Not three months of EKG employment bliss had passed when Marina began to complain that her new job did not satisfy her.

"I know I was excited with this work in the beginning, and I like to work with people, especially with those who are sick and need help," she explained, "but the work I perform now is mechanical and monotonous. I am not going to be an EKG technician for the rest of my life. I want a challenging job where I can use my intelligence."

Whether it was a miracle or not I do not know, but soon she found what she was looking for. Marina's friend in the personnel department of the hospital where she worked told her that there was an opening for a programmer in the computer department of the same hospital and recommended that she apply for the opportunity. In 1975, computer-related disciplines were on a strong rise, and most programmers of that generation were self-taught. The world was quickly moving toward universal computerization, and specialists of any quality in this field were in critical demand then. Marina did not hide her skepticism about the opportunity to be hired, since she'd had limited exposure to programming when she had worked as a scientist at Odessa Higher Engineering Marine School. There, she had worked on a primitive first-generation computer and barely knew anything about computer advancements in the world.

The head of the computer department, who interviewed her, understood right away that Marina was practically computer illiterate. Nevertheless, he conditionally hired her with a probation period of two months. As he explained to Marina later, there were two reasons he hired her. First, there was a great need for a programmer in the computer department, and second, nobody wanted to work for the low salary that the hospital was offering. However, I think the main reason Marina was hired was for her outgoing

life-asserting personality. Within a short time, she had established good relations with most of the people in the department, who then helped her to
become an educated programmer. Not only did she gain professional skills
quickly, but she also loved her new specialty. She learned everything from
simply doing it. Her natural talents allowed her to develop adequate skills just
from diving into the actual work. I do not remember ever seeing any books
on computer science in our house. When I would express my surprise at her
ability to learn everything just from practical experience, her typical answer
was that there are many other important things in this life besides work.

Time passed, and she began to receive tempting offers from headhunt-
ers, specialists who matched businesses with prospective employees. In two
years, she, an immigrant who had recently arrived in this country with two
pieces of luggage and fifteen dollars in her pocket, was working as a computer support specialist in one of the state computers centers. Her salary became
sizable, and even better were the benefits—bonuses, vacations of different
types, and medical insurance. As in any other state organization, it was a
stable job where she could work until retirement. However, Marina was not
a total fan of her new work. For her, a job should be interesting and exciting;
it should open new frontiers in the profession she had chosen. What she was
doing at her present job was mostly simple, routine programming that was
not terribly challenging.

After a short search, she easily found a new job at CNA, a large insurance company, where she ended up working for over thirty years until she retired in 2008. Starting from the lowest position in the data department, she
became a computer engineer in several years, with a salary that was always
higher than her physician husband's. For many years, Marina had responsibilities that required her to be on work calls during nights. In our bedroom, we had two dedicated phone lines—one for my patients and another
for Marina's work. Most nights one or both of us, with equal frequency,
received numerous work-related calls. After a telephone conversation, each
of us would go back to sleep without any problem. Marina was a champion
at falling asleep after receiving one of these numerous night calls. I would
fall asleep when my head touched the pillow, but Marina was already asleep
on her way to the pillow. Insomnia was an unknown entity for both of us.

While Marina was accumulating advanced knowledge in her profession, she never betrayed her principle that learning belonged only to the time when she was at work. When once again I expressed my surprise about her casual attitude toward her profession, she patiently enlightened me that computer science was a vast discipline without borders, and her habit was to learn only what she actually needed, and that amount of useful information she easily absorbed at work.

"I believe work is very important, Vovka," she told me, "but you keep saying the same thing all the time and cannot understand that in addition to work, there is also life. I must have time to take care of our son and our home, for example. And I cannot envision life without visiting our friends, reading my favorite novels, going to the movies, theater, and opera. Life is temporary, and while we are alive, we have this incredible opportunity to learn fascinating things about the world where we live. It gives me great pleasure."

Thanks to Marina's friendly and positive attitude toward life, she was respected and never had enemies among those who worked with her. On several occasions, she was offered managerial positions, but she always declined promotion. "First of all, I hate controlling people," she would say when I asked her why she refused a tempting opportunity. "Besides, I enjoy work where I can learn something new every day. If I become a manager, I won't not be able to update myself with new developments in my field." Being a friendly person, nevertheless, she knew how to stand up for herself. She believed that a bully needed to be confronted with a resolute response. Like any other employee working in a large corporation, she periodically received an official employee evaluation by her managers. Once, she received a poor assessment from a manager who had been recently hired. She went straight to his office and asked him why he was not pleased with her work. When using different platitudes, he tried to get rid of her. Instead of asking him for a better evaluation, Marina confronted him, demanding the truth. She showed the manager a stack of her earlier evaluations, all of which presented her in a positive way. Challenging the manager, she impressed him to such a degree that going forward, he never forgot to greet her since then, and when it came time for evaluation, he was careful to be objective toward her work performance.

Bill, Marina's direct manager, was a thirty-year-old man and a graduate from the University of Chicago. His professors there appreciated him for his dedication and for his remarkable mind. When he was twenty, he had gone swimming with his parents in South Carolina. One fateful day, he dove off a cliff and broke his back, which resulted in a paralyzing injury. Since then, he had been unable to walk and had problems with his bladder function. But he did not let any of that stop him. He managed to graduate from the prestigious university and then was hired by the same insurance company where Marina worked. Being a talented person, he quickly rose to the position of leading project manager. His severe disability did not prevent him from marrying a nurse who loved and cherished him.

Marina and Bill were good friends. For many years, Marina would push her boss's wheelchair, and they would spend their lunch breaks together in the cafeteria. In 2000, Bill developed urosepsis, a condition related to the poor functioning of his bladder. This severe condition had an added complication of his fingertips' necrosis. Majority of people in his place would have given up, but not Bill. In the two months before he returned to work, he had already developed a way of working on the computer's keyboard. To compensate for the loss of fingertips, he worked using a pencil that he grasped between his remaining fingers.

Over the years, Marina and Bill enjoyed each other's company, and even after she was diagnosed with metastatic cancer, she continued to help her friend with mobility. When circumstances allowed, she would give Bill a ride in his wheelchair outside the insurance building, which was located in downtown Chicago.

Different Paths to Faith

Meanwhile, following our mutual desire to spend time together as much as possible in our ever-busy lives, about a year after Marina started to attend synagogue religious service, I began to join her whenever I was free from duties at the hospital. Gradually, going to the synagogue for Sabbath services became our joint endeavor. While I did not hesitate to discuss themes about God, religion, or the Bible with Marina, she hardly ever reciprocated. Her religious belief was deep inside, and it never left her. Only at the end of her life did I have an opportunity to understand the degree of her faith. In our life together, Marina's faith manifested in her striving to adhere to some of religious traditions. She never preached her personal religion to anybody and did not share it with anybody, me included, but soon acceptance of religion in her outlook became an indelible part of her life. Never trying to proselytize, Marina introduced into our family Jewish dietary laws and the observance of Shabbat. Nobody had persuaded her, a former agnostic, to regularly attend the synagogue's services. It was her own decision.

Despite our close relationship, Marina never demonstrated any wish to discuss the real essence of her belief with me. Her intuitive faith was based on the voice of her heart, which is impossible to express in human language. She kept her faith to herself and never discussed it voluntarily with anybody, including me, her closest friend. For myself I explained her silence was due her perception that the basic theological subjects for her was so sacred that it was beyond words. Being introverted on this subject did not prevent her from actively taking part in temple group discussions about different religious subjects. With her good memory, she remembered episodes and events described in the Five Books of Moses better than many people, including me.

Challenges in life often compel people to come to religion as a mighty tool in coping with tough life realities. To our numerous agnostic friends who were asking me why I believed in God, I responded with a counterquestion: "If not in God, then in what do you believe?" To this simple and legitimate question, I never heard a satisfactory answer.

Marina and I never stopped enjoying each other's company. Following the natural inclination that genuine friends do things together, I tried not to miss an opportunity to join her at the weekly Shabbat service. As another year or two passed, she--it was always Marina who opened new pages in our everyday dealings with the spiritual world--expanded our observation of the

Jewish rituals. We began to observe Shabbat not only during the synagogue's services but in our house as well. Sincere in the expression of her religious views, Marina never tried to appear more religious than she was and never tried to draw anybody into religion. Living with the idea of God was natural for her and unobtrusive to friends and outsiders.

On Friday nights, we began to light candles and said our prayers. Our prayers, as in any other observant Jewish family, were followed by a delicious meal prepared by the hostess of the house. Observation of Shabbat turned out to be much easier than we thought in the beginning. Moreover, it became an enjoyable experience. Marina continued to be the undeclared leader in our further immersion in Jewish traditions. This brought new developments into our lives. We were busy individuals, so if one of us was on duty or at work then the ritual was observed by the remaining spouse and our son. The introduction of each new detail of the religious ritual, which initially appeared to us as an impossible undertaking, became quite a simple thing with the help of our religious friends. As there were no kosher grocery stores around us, Marina started to make regular trips to Chicago's northern suburbs to shop.

Family Reunification

In 1979, the rest of my family—my mother, my brother, and his wife and two children—arrived in the United States from the Soviet Union. On the day of their arrival, Marina, Sasha, and I went to meet them at O'Hare Airport in Chicago. The plane arrived on time, and the first person whom I saw was my seventy-three-year-old mother dressed in an old-fashioned coat and a worn shawl. I was distressed to see her looking much older than the last time I had seen her, when we left the Soviet Union. Now, five years later, she appeared shorter, and her face was covered with a web of wrinkles. When my mother smiled, I noticed that some of her teeth were missing. Walking next to her were my brother and his family. As it could be expected, after the years of separation, our long-awaited reunion was emotional and joyous.

At first, the newcomers lived with us in our apartment in uptown Chicago. Later, my brother's family moved to an apartment in Chicago's Rogers Park, while my mother lived in a separate apartment one door down from us.

Manya, the Family Cat

After visiting our good friends in Cincinnati, Ohio, we adopted a lovely stray female cat whose name nobody knew, so we gave her the easy-to-pronounce name Manya. She was a noble cat with long, gray fur and smart eyes. At the beginning, she had problems adapting to indoor life in a strictly domestic environment. We tried to resist her demands to spend time outside, but she did not stop protesting, meowing and scratching the entrance door. Eventually, I said that we must respect the wishes of the animal that had grown up on the streets and could not live without being outside. Our female cat needed her freedom, and the value of freedom is above everything else. If, God forbid, something should happen to her, we would just have to live with that. After that, Manya became a free agent. Since then, we allowed her to be outside until she returned home on her own.

One wrong thing we did when we adopted her. Not having any experience of dealing with pets, we followed the advice of our friends, who strongly recommended that we remove the claws from the cat. When we did it, we did not understand that a cat who enjoys outdoors needs claws when it comes to fighting with other cats or animals at night. Declawing deprived our cat of precious ammunition against her competition with the other wild and domesticated cats in our neighborhood. Manya compensated for the defect with her qualities as a warrior. She was a great fighter, and night after night, she proved her dominating position among the animals' outdoor society. Regretfully, nobody is perfect, and our legendary cat was no exception to this rule. Some nights, Manya would lose her next fight with "politically incorrect" animals, resulting in wounds to her furry skin that required a visit to the veterinarian.

In the warm season, when the weather allowed it, we slept with the windows open on the second floor. So, one night, from hearing her frightened sounds, we knew Manya was losing her nightly battle. Before I could think of what should be done, Marina, a dedicated protector of our cat, whom she treated as part of our family, dressed only in her nightgown, was already downstairs and then in the backyard, saving our pet. Returning from outside, she was holding fighter Manya tightly to her chest.

Once when I was still at work, Marina heard the mournful meowing of our cat coming from our attic. Using a flashlight, she found that Manya had fallen into a narrow closed-in space between the roof's edge and the wall along one side of the attic. The cat had landed at least a foot down from the opening, but Marina, after much effort and lying on her stomach for a substantial time, was able to bring the animal up from the trap.

Surrounded by loving care, our cat, Manya, lived with us for about twenty years. In the last years of her life, she became domesticated and socialized. Both Marina and I had a habit of speaking to Manya as if she were another human being. For most of her life, the cat was silently listening to us talking to her, and then suddenly, to our big surprise, in her older years, she began to respond in her own feline manner, as if trying to communicate to us what was on her mind. After that, when one of us addressed Manya, she answered sometimes with a series of unarticulated primitive but expressive sounds, as if she wanted to share with us what was her feline opinion on the subject. Like a small child, she could not verbally express herself, but her mind was there.

Though our cat's IQ score was gaining points, her aging body began to develop some ailments, the most unpleasant being a urinary tract infection that required treatment with antibiotics. To give her a tablet, I would tightly hold the cat while Marina, unclenching her jaw with a dexterous movement, dropped the pill into her mouth. Our cat eventually developed urine incontinence, and yellow spots began to appear on our recently installed white carpet. But Marina loved our cat too much to show any signs of annoyance with the messes. Initially, she tried to get rid of yellow spots with all kinds of recommended shampoos, which were not as effective as we'd hoped. Eventually, devoted to our cat, Marina hired workers to remove the new carpet. We were left with wooden parquet floors, which were much easier to clean.

When our smart cat had reached a venerable age, we were with her at the time of her death in our bedroom, after which we carefully wrapped her body in a cloth and buried her in our garden.

Sealing Marriage in Heaven

After graduating from my residency in 1982, I joined a private pediatric practice in one of Chicago's western suburbs. To be close to my patients and to the hospitals where I was accredited and where I was periodically on call at the ER, we moved to a western suburb. There we bought a house, and my mother moved in with us again, this time under the same roof, and what a golden time it was.

We joined the local Conservative Jewish Synagogue, where we became regular participants in religious activities, one of which was a communal gathering called Kallah. During Kallah, members of the congregation came together to become immersed in religious life. Our synagogue's Kallah took place in resort cabins in Wisconsin Dells for the day of rest, the Shabbat celebration. We had gone for a few years and enjoyed the time there very much. A few weeks before the 1985 Kallah, during the religious service, the rabbi asked the congregation what ideas they had for the centerpiece of the Kallah activity.

When we returned home from the synagogue, during supper, Marina, giving me a mysterious look, told me that she had a great idea.

"What kind of idea?" I asked.

"Do you remember, Vovka, that back in the Soviet Union, where we knew nothing about religion, we only had a civil marriage? Wouldn't it be great if we celebrate our religious marriage during Kallah? Would you have anything against that?"

Who could object to such a brilliant idea? I agreed without hesitation, and we let our rabbi know about Marina's idea a day later. The rabbi accepted our suggestion with enthusiasm. At his request, volunteer experts from the synagogue began to collect the items needed for our wedding ceremony.

Two weeks later, at least fifty members of the congregation arrived at Perlman Center in Wisconsin Dells early in the morning on a Friday. In the evening, when the day of rest had just started, all who were taking part in the ceremony came to the center's club. Following the traditional Shabbat service, the rabbi beckoned to Marina and me to join him on the stage—*bimah* in Hebrew. Then our son, my brother with his wife, and four members of the congregation who'd been invited by us joined us there. The time had come for Marina and me to obtain a religious status to our eleven years of civil marriage, which, as religious tradition teaches, guarantees that the souls of the bride and the groom will find each other and reunite in heaven.

When the religious ceremony began, the rabbi invited Marina and me, as bride and groom, to stand under a *chuppah*, a portable canopy held aloft by four poles. For the canopy, a *tallit*—a prayer shawl—was used. The ritual fringes (*tzitzit*) on the prayer shawl held above the couple's heads serve as a reminder of the commandments (*mitzvot*) and are regarded as a talisman against evil spirits. The poles of *chuppah* were held by my brother, his wife, and two of our synagogue friends. After that, as had been done for millennia, according to the tradition, my bride, my beautiful wife, walked around me, the groom, seven times. According to Jeremiah 31:22, "A woman shall surround a man."

Then came time to exchange our rings. By then, we had already worn them for eleven years. The most exciting moment of the ceremony happened when to the applause of all the congregants, I broke a glass wrapped in a napkin with my foot. The breaking of the glass symbolizes the destruction of the Jewish temple in Jerusalem and the absolute conclusiveness of the marital covenant. The guests shouted "Mazel tov!" and "Congratulations!" and the rabbi congratulated us both. Accompanied by applause, we left the stage, now a full-fledged, super-legitimate wife and husband consecrated by the laws of the Jewish religion.

"Now God is entirely on our side, for sure," my dear bride informed me, giving me her divine smile.

Our life was happy, secure, and predictable. We had good jobs and good friends, our son was successfully studying, and fortune was smiling on us. America had opened its doors to the opportunities about which we only could dream before. Our marital bliss was full. We knew how to love each other and lived in harmony, hardly ever misunderstanding each other.

The Trouble with the Mother

But nothing lasts forever.

One day in the fall of 1985, with great embarrassment, my mother confessed to me that she felt a swelling not far from her perineal area. She'd had it for a while, but she had been ashamed to tell me, her son, about this ominous finding. The next day, I took her to an experienced and trusted surgeon. Sitting in the waiting room, I was nervous. In a quarter of an hour, the door opened, and the surgeon came out with a tense expression on his face. What he said burned my heart painfully. It turned out my mother had advanced cancer, which at this stage probably was metastatic. Cancer was a menacing word in our family; seventeen years ago, my father had died from liver cancer. Now it was my mother's turn to become its victim.

Two days later, an oncologist confirmed the surgeon's diagnosis. In two weeks, the biopsy verified the diagnosis beyond any doubt, and my mother was admitted to the hospital for her first chemotherapy treatment.

Her attending oncologist, when I would meet him during my morning rounds in the same hospital, greeted me with a friendly and optimistic smile. "Your mother will be okay. We are doing our best to help her," he assured me on many occasions. "Last week I read a paper dedicated to a new treatment for the type of tumor your mother has. She is receiving treatment according to the latest recommendations. I hope we are going to see the same good result as the authors of the article achieved with their patients."

In the beginning, my mother tolerated chemotherapy surprisingly well. After two months of treatment, she began radiation therapy, performed in a hospital not too far from our house. Initially, she was strong enough to walk there by herself, but later a lack of energy prevented her from walking there.

After the first course of radiation therapy ended, the oncologist prescribed a second round, which, for technical reasons, was supposed to take place at a university hospital located in downtown Chicago. Getting there required the use of a car, so for the next six weeks, either Marina or I transported my mother there for her medical appointments.

Unexpectedly, a month later when the second course of radiation treatments was almost over, I accidentally met my mother's attending oncological radiologist, a middle-aged, friendly-looking man. He started a conversation with me about my mother's health status. Believing the maxim that a physician might sometimes not be able to help but that after a visit to him a patient ought to feel more encouraged, I was ready to hear from the doctor something reassuring about my mother's prognosis. With a kind smile, that never left his face, he told me that he expected that my still strong-looking mother would not live longer than another two or one month. Looking forward, the physician was wrong. My mother was blessed to live for another six months.

From many friends and acquaintances, I learned that irresponsible statements of this kind from medics are a frequent occurrence, especially in the field of oncology. Unfortunately, the rule that physicians should encourage and motivate patients and their families is not applicable to all physicians. Frequently, whatever the physicians tell patients and caregivers about their impression of the patient's condition depends on the physician's personality. There are those who are gentle in their pronouncements, and there are those who do not hesitate to tell patients and their families "the truth" to their face, even if this "truth" might be mistaken or premature. During my pediatric residency, I noticed this type of peculiar behavior on the part of some medical students. They would do nothing when good news came about a patient, but they would run to the patient's hospital room with bad news, scaring him or her and their family. Who knows, maybe they were unconsciously wanting to see the unpleasant reactions of those they informed about bad news—or, more probable, they felt themselves powerful because with their words, they could have such a strong negative impact on people they hardly knew.

After the course of treatment with chemotherapy and radiotherapy was over, my mother's oncologist was less optimistic than he was initially. Nevertheless, he reassured her and me that the outcome might be promising.

Despite all the treatment my mother received, unfortunately, her cancer continued its "triumphant pace" in her body. Soon she developed metastases in her inner organs. Gradually her condition worsened, and eventually she was confined for twenty hours a day to a rented hospital bed in her bedroom. For pain, the oncologist prescribed her a morphine solution, which Marina or I regularly gave her by mouth. Soon, the metastatic spread produced an obstruction in her lower bowels, hindering bowel movements. That complication required surgical intervention. In two days, my mother returned home with an ileostomy, which is a surgical opening in the abdominal wall. The ileostomy is a way to release the bowel content from the small intestine. When my mother was discharged to go home, the hospital provided us with all necessary items to take care of the opening or stoma. Because I was very busy with my pediatric practice, it was mostly Marina who, as a devoted daughter would, was taking care of the unpleasant tasks related to my mother's ileostomy. To make my mother more comfortable and to try not to wake me up after a difficult day at my office, it was Marina who would run downstairs to the first floor to perform the necessary medical interventions on my mother in the middle of the night.

My mother died nine months after she was diagnosed with cancer. The immediate cause of her death was superficial bleeding from the femoral artery, produced by one of the cancer metastases. Thanks to the morphine that we gave her from a bottle in the prescribed doses, she died without pain and suffering, surrounded by the members of her family.

Such is life, that there comes a time when people dear to us are destined to leave this world. Those who stay alive must continue to live and enjoy their wholesome life. This is how our world works.

Sports and Other Entertainment

Marina was a strong woman. She had never taken part in organized sports, but she liked hiking and going to dance lessons. In the winter of 1989, when she was forty-eight years old, she slipped on the ice as she returned home from work and partially ruptured her Achilles tendon. When she was recovering from the trauma, her orthopedic surgeon recommended that she walk using a moderately high-heeled shoe. Being a motivated patient, she took the advice appropriately, and almost daily for an hour or more she walked on the streets of the neighborhood after returning from her job. Her devotion to such a regimen paid off, and in a couple of months, her Achilles tendon was fully healed, and her leg muscles were strong enough to allow her to walk without any problem. The orthopedic surgeon again congratulated Marina for the excellent outcome. Marina's devotion paid off, and a year later, she was able to attend dance class once again at the local private dance studio.

Busy with my numerous doctor's responsibilities, I could not join her in her activity. Marina loved to dance and attended the class for at least thirteen years, until she began her first treatment for breast cancer.

For many years, Marina and I enjoyed walking together in our neighborhood. The pattern of our walks was always the same. Initially, Marina, in accord with her enthusiastic character, overtook me by several yards, stopping from time to time so that I could catch up. Then, for a while, we walked next to each other, but by the end of the hike, she grew tired, so I walked quicker than she did.

One of the sports Marina liked was scuba diving. We learned how to dive in the Grand Cayman Island in 1981, when we went there on vacation along with Alexander. A sign we saw outside one of the coastal shops advertised that their experienced instructor taught scuba diving and promised that at the end of the course, participants would receive a genuine international scuba diving license. Marina enthusiastically supported my suggestion that we should take the class in scuba diving. There were three more couples in our class. The instructor was excellent. He watched us like a hen watches her chicks while teaching us all the skills necessary for safe scuba diving. Our group's lessons were productive, and on the fourth day, we were already diving at a nearby reef, the beauty of which was outstanding. We took many pictures underwater to show later to our relatives and friends. Our instructor praised Marina on couple of occasions, telling our group that Marina was his best student.

Since that time, we have enjoyed scuba diving during many vacation trips to the Caribbean islands and Mexico. Several years later, in 1986, again together with our then-nineteen-year-old son, for our vacation, we went to Cozumel, Mexico. On the third day after our arrival, we decided to go for a group scuba. On a boat equipped with the necessary gear, we arrived at a reef located far from shore. There were twelve people in the group, including the instructor and two boat crew members. In the group was an attractive, young American woman who was openly wooed by our instructor. Like two birds, the couple did not stop chatting their bird talk. I had heard before that sport instructors in Mexico at that time were much less attentive to the safety of tourists than those in the US or the Cayman Islands. The main reason was the tourists' lack of the local information. The local newspapers in the Mexican resorts were available only in Spanish, and because of the language barrier, tourists did not have any idea about tragic accidents that occurred in the area. Visitors who stayed at Mexican hotels were not informed about all kinds of incidents, including accidents and food poisoning. In the USA, epidemiological services could easily establish the reason for an outbreak of gastrointestinal infections, which would result in the immediate closure of the restaurant responsible for it. But in Mexico, tourists did not know about recent health-related accidents that had taken place in the area, so they were not worried about possible dangerous problems.

Ten minutes before diving, our instructor began routine preparations with us at the reef. From the beginning, it was clear that he did not care much about his primary responsibilities. Before we went in the water, he gave the group brief instructions, then he was the last to dive in. During the dive, both crew members remained on the boat. When in the water, the instructor assembled the entire group and, using gestures, ordered everyone to follow him. Unfortunately, after this instruction, he dedicated all his attention to the beautiful American girl, whom he was treating as if she were the only one for whom he was responsible. Without the instructor's attention, the members of the group were doing their own activity, enjoying the wealth of beauty of the underwater coral reef with all kinds of seaweed and fish. Marina and Sasha were close to me, each of them fascinated with the beautiful details of the coral reef. Ten minutes went by before I realized that the regulator supplying me with air from the tank on my back was defective. Not wanting to disturb Marina and Sasha, without success, I tried to fix the device for the following three or four minutes. While I was doing this, with each minute, it was becoming harder for me to breathe. Soon Marina and Sasha noticed that I had a problem. While preoccupied with the young woman, our instructor was nowhere to be found. Marina and Sasha, together with me, were trying to make my regulator work.

Seeing that all attempts to take care of the problem were fruitless, I was ready to surface when Marina touched my shoulder, decisively removed her regulator from her face, and tried to offer it to me. I shook my head in protest, and with a hand gesture, signaled her that I was on my way to the surface. Marina and Sasha, who were now close to me, understood my gesture, and went with me all the way up. When my head was above the waves, I removed the regulator from my mouth and at once realized how restless the sea was that day. With the regulator now on my neck, the choppy waves were choking me, not letting me breathe normally. Marina and my son were trying to help me, but I could not avoid the waves that choked me one after another.

As I fought for air, I turned my head, trying to see the boat that had brought us to the reef. I finally saw it, rocking on waves, a hundred meters away from us. The sound of the waves drowned out my screams for help. I began to wave my hands, trying to grab the attention of the two crewmen, who were involved in conversation. One of them finally noticed my gestures. For some reason, the crewman, whose first responsibility was the safety of the divers, perceived my behavior as funny and started laughing while pointing a finger in my direction. Now both the crewmen laughed together. Eventually, he realized that something was wrong. Turning on the motor and approaching me, one of the crewmen stretched out his hand to help me and then to Marina and Sasha.

Remembering this unforgettable episode now, I cannot forget how ignoring her own safety being deep underwater, Marina did not think twice before trying to help me, when she removed the regulator from her mouth and insisted that I breathe from it. Ever since I married my wife, it never ceased to surprise me how she never hesitated to help me and those who were in trouble. After the described episode, I emphatically thanked her for help, but she only shrugged and remained silent, as if nothing had happened. When I insisted on praising her, she became visibly disturbed and told me to shut up. In the fifty-six years of living with this woman who was straight as an arrow, I do not remember a single episode when she ever fished for compliments.

Marina and I liked to spend time together, but there was one activity where she could not join me—my favorite sport, bicycling. I loved cycling from an early age, but for Marina, a large-city dweller, it was a sport she had never tried. Since she did not even know how to ride a bike, she remained at home, busy with her own activities, while I went for bicycle trips.

One summer evening of 1982, I returned from day-long bike trip. Later, during supper, Marina turned to me with an unexpected request, which reminded me of an episode when the narrator in the Nikos Kazantzakis' novel asks Zorba the Greek to teach him how to dance. "Tomorrow you will start teaching me how to ride a bike," she said in a voice that brooked no objection.

"Are you crazy, Marina?" I said, not hiding my surprise. "Why do you want to ride a bicycle? Sorry to remind you, but next year you will be forty."

"Very simple," she answered, now looking into my eyes. "It's not fair that I am left without you while you go for your bicycle trips. I know you love to ride your bicycle, and by no means do I want to keep you from it. So, the only way for us to spend more time together is for me to learn how to ride too. And for your information, I am not forty yet, and I am still young enough to learn this skill."

Love is known to be a two-way road. To deserve love, each spouse must bring an equal contribution to the relationship. My wife's desire to learn how to ride a bicycle made me feel proud that there was a woman in this world who appreciated me so much that she was ready to learn a new, difficult skill in order spend time with me.

The next day, we started our classes. Since then, almost daily, we spent one or more hours practicing in a parking lot close to our house. As it could be expected, Marina went through a difficult time learning how to keep balance on a bicycle. With all the patience in the world, time after time, she made attempts to ride it, only to lose her balance and endure another fall, until the unforgettable moment finally came when she was able to tame the "stubborn bicycle" and gained enough confidence to ride it. She never achieved perfection in riding. For example, for better balance, her saddle needed to be in a position that was too low for her height, and she had to get off the bicycle each time it was necessary to make a sharp turn. However, what mattered was that she finally learned to ride a bike for long distances. It stays only to add that it is a great source of joy when your best friend is riding next to you on a bicycle excursion.

In 1984, Marina and I decided to undertake a long bike trip of approximately three hundred miles. It was many years before the sweeping electronic intrusion of GPS, so we used bicycle road maps. After long deliberation, we concluded that the most suitable route for us would be from the city of La Crosse on the Mississippi River in Western Wisconsin all the way to Chicago. Especially for this trip, we bought two brand-new Miyata bicycles with the necessary accessories. Taking along only the minimal essentials for travel, we sent our bicycles as cargo on the same train we rode to La Crosse. It was early evening when we arrived. We retrieved our bicycles at the railroad station and rode on them to the hotel where we'd reserved a room beforehand. With the front-desk manager's permission, we brought our bicycles to our hotel room for safekeeping and went to a nearby restaurant for lunch. The rest of the day and evening we spent in preparation for the next day's ride.

Early in the morning, we started our long journey in the state of Wisconsin. From La Crosse to Sparta-Elroy, we rode along a bicycle trail that in the past had been a railroad line. The rest of the trip took us through New Glarus, Sauk City, Mount Horeb, and Rockford and Chicago in Illinois. Marina, then forty years young, strong and dedicated, was in excellent physical shape and complained about physical exhaustion only once, on the last day of our trip riding to Chicago from Rockford, where we had met up with old friends.

On that last day, after a nice sleepover and a hearty breakfast in the morning in Rockford, our host gave us a twenty-mile ride in his car toward Chicago. The rest of the day's sixty-seven miles we rode on our bicycles. This went well until we reached Lombard, a suburb of metropolitan Chicago, al-most the last point of our tour. Here, Marina put her foot down: she refused to go further due to the heavy traffic and --uncharacteristic of her--started to cry. It was not the distance between where we were now and our home, but the number of cars on the road that made her afraid. She was worried we could be in an accident on the busy street. So, we called a taxi to take Marina home while I continued to ride to our house, where she was waiting for me. We were proud of our athletic achievement and enjoyed many photos from this trip.

It was impossible not to adore my friend in life during the bicycle trip. It had only been a short time since she'd learned to ride a bicycle, and she had been able to cycle such a long way on this trip, which, not counting one for me and three for her falls, went without serious accidents.

Several years later, in 1989, Marina and I took another long bicycle trip, again in Wisconsin. We loaded our Miyata bicycles on our Blazer's rack and in three and half hours arrived at a hotel in the city of Waupaca, in the Chain O'Lakes region. Over the next few days, we enjoyed exploring the many cycle paths in the area. The last day of our vacation, we spent riding the Ice Age National Scenic Trail in Hartman Creek State Park, a pictur-esque, quiet, and friendly place.

At the end of the day, we prepared to return to our hotel. Consulting a map, instead of riding together as we usually did, I decided to do something different. Marina would take a shorter way, and since I was a faster rider, I would take a longer path. Along the way, I took delight in the pleasing views. Unexpectedly, the route I had taken was so scenic that I figured I would catch up on travel time by riding at a greater speed to the park's exit and meanwhile I will click several beautiful pictures. Having taken the last photo, I got on the bicycle and, full of energy and strength, rode toward our arranged meeting place. After twenty minutes of cycling, I realized that a ranger service car was approaching me from behind. When it caught up with me, it stopped abruptly, the door opened, and my wife jumped out of the vehicle. Two smiling rangers followed her.

Marina's pale face was distorted from crying, and she was wiping tears—a very rare case when she expressed such an emotion. "How dare you travel so long!" she yelled at me. "I was patiently waiting for you, but you weren't coming. Why did you take so long? Did you not think about me? I was so worried! You did not give me any other choice but to ask these nice gentlemen, these rangers, to help me to find you!"

While I was apologizing, trying to explain to Marina that I was only a few minutes late, one of the rangers, who was in his late forties, came up to us. "Look at this couple," he said with a wide smile on his face. "The husband is maybe only ten minutes late, and his poor wife is already hysterical. I wish my wife were as sensitive as yours, pal," he told me. "My dear spouse does not much care if I come home even hours later than the appointed time. You should have seen your wife when she asked us to look for you. She was almost shaking from fear. You are a lucky guy to have a wife who cares so much about you."

The ranger was only telling me something I knew well. What is better than to have a devoted friend, especially if it is your wife?

Marina cared for all those who were dear to her heart, which included animals as well. Two years after our bicycle trip to Waupaca, our cat, Manya, disappeared and did not return home for four days. We both worried about our beloved pet, but she was nowhere to be found. Eventually, in an attempt to find her, Marina went to one of the nearby alleys to search, without success calling the cat's name. After an hour Marina saw our cat, Manya. To her dismay, the cat was covered with numerous abrasions and bloodstains from the previous street fight. At the sight of Marina, she meowed pitifully and did not resist when Marina took her in arms and ran with her to home, where she treated the cat's wound and gave her a good bath.

Vasomotor Hot Flashes

In the early 1990s, apart from persistent and unpleasant hot flashes, Marina was a healthy woman, who was now in her late forties. Hot flashes, a curse that afflicts many women who are going through menopause, produce a sudden sensation of heat in the chest, face, and head, followed by flushing, perspiration, and sometimes chills. Menopause-related hot flashes and night sweats can last for years, and an effective treatment is difficult to come by. Over-the-counter remedies help only for mild cases.

Marina's hot flashes began when she was approaching the age of fifty. Initially, they were tolerable and did not require special treatment. The use of over-the-counter remedies also did not bring success. Typical for many cases, gradually the frequency and intensity of her hot flashes became unbearable until it began to greatly affect her life. Eventually she did not have other choice but to resort to estrogen replacement therapy. Treatment with estrogen, normal level of which is universally reduced in menopausal women, is the most effective treatment for hot flashes.

Estrogen is a female sex hormone produced mainly by the ovaries. The therapy with it works like magic, effectively helping women live a normal life. Unfortunately, for every useful deed, it is necessary to pay. In the case of estrogen hormone replacement therapy, the price of its use is a predisposition to ovarian, uterine, and breast cancer. However, considering the pros and cons, or, as it's called, the benefit-to-harm ratio, standard medical practice clearly dictates the use of estrogen in severe cases of hot flashes, which Marina had. She did her best-- but without success--to stay away from estrogen therapy by trying all kinds of alternative treatments.

In 1995, we took a vacation to Florida, where we stayed in one of the Hollywood Beach hotels. We were then in one of the nearby state parks for swimming and sunbathing when Marina, whose hot flashes by then were happening almost every hour, was unusually pale and lacking energy.

"Can't you see what's happening to me? Aren't you a doctor, or what?" she addressed me with stern rebuke in her voice. "Do something, and quickly."

From a public phone on the beach, I contacted Marina's gynecologist. After I described him the symptoms, he told me that my wife definitely needed estrogen therapy treatment. The estrogen pills that I bought from one of the local pharmacies worked like magic. It was simply amazing how, literally before my eyes, Marina's condition drastically improved. But even as we were admiring its action, we were aware of the potential risk for cancer. Since then, Marina used the hormone therapy on a regular basis, although time after time she tried to manage her hot flashes without it. After reviewing a lot of literature, we tried to use the alternative methods that could help her cope with hot flashes. But nothing except the hormone replacement produced anything even close to the desired effect. Unfortunately, there was nothing else to do but to give in and admit that only the estrogen was able to prevent the debilitating symptoms of this awful curse.

CHAPTER 2

In the Eye of the Storm

The Procedure for Introducing the Localization Wire

Now it is time to return to the events surrounding that terrible day in September 2005 when Marina--at the time she was almost sixty-two--told me that possibly she had breast cancer. Three days after that fateful conversation, we visited the imaging department of the local community hospital where I was an attending physician. By this point, I had been retired from the hospital for almost two years. This allowed Marina to have me as a steady companion, who would go with her to the countless doctors' visits, procedures, and imaging studies that were to come. For many years, I learned countless times how important a companion's role was in prolonging the life of a patient. And that's how I transformed myself into Marina's shadow, following her faithfully through the unending chain of medical procedures.

The reason for the visit at the community hospital imaging department was for a wire localization procedure, in which a radiologist, with the help of a fluoroscope, inserts a wire into the place where the tumor is present. The goal of this procedure is to help the surgeon localize and remove the tumor during the surgery. The procedure was performed by a radiologist in his forties who appeared to be friendly and polite. However, appearances are deceiving. It did not take long for me to realize that for all his experience, the radiologist completely lacked an ability to see in his patients living human beings. As Shakespeare said, "if you prick us, do we not bleed?" For some reason, he decided that the placement of a wire deep in a breast could be done without local anesthesia.

Prepared for the intervention, Marina seated on a special chair, ready for the procedure. I could see the progress of the procedure standing next to her. The radiologist filled a large syringe with a solution, inserted the thin wire into long and wide needle, and was ready to inject this needle into Marina's breast tissue. Incredulous, I asked him if he was not planning to give to the patient a local anesthetic prior to insertion.

"Oh, don't worry, Doctor. Actually, it is a very quick and practically painless procedure, so I never use anesthesia," he reassured me with a confident smile.

Gently, radiologist inserted the needle with wire in it deep inside the breast tissue, but at that instant, exactly what I was afraid might happen indeed happened. Marina suddenly became pale, and in another moment, she fainted. She began to slip off the chair and would have fallen hard if I had not caught her by her shoulders.

The radiologist, who did not appear the least bit guilty, sorry, or surprised, sat on his stool, serenely looking at the patient. Helped by two nurses who were also in the room, I lifted Marina from the floor and placed her on a couch. In a short time, she regained consciousness, although she remained very pale. We helped her take a seat once again on the chair in front of the fluoroscope. As if nothing had happened, and without hint of apology or regret, the radiologist this time applied local anesthesia and resumed the procedure without further incident.

Despite the assurances of the radiologist, who after the procedure tried to convince me that fainting during the procedure was rare in his experience, I did not believe him. Later, from other patients who had gone through the same procedure, I learned that this radiologist had a careless attitude and did not want to spend his "valuable" time applying local anesthesia. If medicine is supposed to be a humane profession, then respect for the natural fragility of patients should be the proper attitude of practitioners. I am sure physicians would never perform that kind of procedure on their own family members without taking the necessary steps for the exposure to pain or trauma.

As a doctor with a specialty far from the field of oncology, I had only a superficial understanding of the questions related to mammography. For example, I thought mammography was a highly reliable diagnostic test. I had no way of knowing that mammography was far from being a precise study. Actually, it is nothing more than a screening test. Ultrasound and MRI scans are much more precise in finding tumors. Mammography is a commonly used diagnostic tool for economic reasons, while ultrasound and MRI scans are used only when the imaging reveals something that needs further investigation.

Starting at fifty years of age, Marina had done her mammogram every year without pathological findings, except for the last one, which uncovered a cancerous growth 4.0 to 4.5 centimeters long. A relatively large size of the tumor meant--as was later confirmed to me by oncologists--that Marina's breast tumor was missed for at least two or three previous years by different radiologists when they read her annual mammograms. Scientific data shows that the less experienced the radiologists are who read and interpret the mammography films, the higher is the chance they can overlook the tumor in the breast. The lack of precision in reading mammograms is an established fact to such a degree that it protects radiologists from malpractice suits.

The large size of Marina's tumor unfortunately meant that she had a high chance of having cancer metastases.

Lumpectomy at the Community Hospital

The next day Marina was examined by Dr. Keller, one of the leading surgeons at the community hospital. Although he was respected for his technical skills, I'd heard from my acquaintances that his bedside manners were not too good. In any case, as the choice was limited, Marina and I decided to ignore this drawback and to take advantage of his professional expertise.

After the examination, Dr. Keller recommended a lumpectomy surgery, during which he would remove the breast's tumor. It is also called breast-conserving surgery, or a wide local excision. During lumpectomy, unlike a mastectomy, only a part of the breast tissues is removed.

A day later, Dr. Keller, with the help of the location wire inserted by the radiologist, removed the cancerous breast tissue, which was sent to the laboratory for histological studies. It takes at least ten days to receive the test results. If they showed that the edges of tissues that were removed were negative or free from malignancy, that meant that the cancer was removed entirely, and no further surgery would be needed.

The result from the histological examination was not available yet when we went for Marina's first visit to the oncologist Dr. Stan Roth, whose private practice office was located not far from the hospital where the lumpectomy had been performed. When we entered Dr. Roth's waiting room, two receptionists greeted us, and one of them handed Marina forms to be filled out. As always, Marina handed me the forms to fill in. I knew if I asked her why I should do this for her, with a sly smile she would answer that I am a doctor, and I would do this kind of work better than she would. Besides, with a sly smirk on her face, she could admit that she was too lazy and impatient to do such a boring job. When I was done with the forms, I looked around and saw that the condition of the waiting room was far from what might be expected for such a place. The waiting room was dusty, the chairs were old and rickety, and, without exception, the paintings on the walls hung askew. This disheveled waiting room is definitely not worthy of its owner, the hospital's leading oncology specialist.

Twenty minutes later, a nurse called us. Nervous and worried, we entered the examination room. With old-fashioned furniture and dirty floors, the examination room looked just as uncomfortable and unhygienic as the waiting room. An ununiformed nurse took Marina's vital signs, asked a few pertinent questions, and handed Marina a paper coat to prepare for the examination. Dr. Roth, on whose face was written the expression of professional arrogance, soon entered the room. His knowledge that the fate of sick people critically depended on him elevated him in his own eyes.

There was an interesting harmony between the mess in the office and the overall impression of our oncologist. He spoke in short, curt sentences and could barely keep meaningful eye contact. Although we met each other almost every day in the hospital, it turned out that Dr. Roth's ego did not allow him to admit that he recognized me. His behavior showed that he lacked the sympathetic feeling even for a patient who had recently been given a potentially fatal diagnosis. Showing no emotion, Dr. Roth asked Marina a few questions. After listening to all the answers, without uttering a word, he went ahead to examine her. In the middle of his examination, when I tried to add important information, Dr. Roth gave me such an icy look that I immediately shut up.

At the end of the examination, it was time for the doctor to summarize his findings.

"Before you came today, I already discussed your case with your surgeon," Dr. Roth said. "From him, I learned that there is a possibility that your tumor has spread more than he initially expected. If the edges of the tumor tissue removed during the surgery will be read by a histologist as positive for malignancy, you will need further surgery," he said. "By the way, it is good that your breast is of such a generous size. That will help the surgeon remove your tumor more effectively."

There was an element of impudence in Dr. Roth's tone when he gave a vulgar characterization of Marina's anatomy that made her blush.

Upon hearing the plethora of bad news, we left Dr. Roth with a sense of emotional strain. At the exit, we approached the receptionists to schedule a follow-up visit. When we approached them, they were too busy to listen to us while they were in the middle of discussing a funny story. Finally, one of them acknowledging our presence, entered information into the computer and handed Marina a card with information about the next visit. Then, ignoring the possibility that the patients before her might have just heard the terrible news about their prognosis, and as if Marina were a child waiting for candy, the receptionist pulled out a pack of ballpoint pens from a desk drawer and handed them to my wife. Judging by the insignia on these pens, they were left by a pharmaceutical companies' representatives as "free goodies," and apparently the secretary was handing them out to patients to get rid of them. Ballpoint pens were just what Marina needed in her grim situation. We left the office in a bad mood and barely said a word to each other until we got home.

Ten days later, we went to see Dr. Keller again. Distractedly, dryly, he casually informed us that the edges of the tumor tissue taken from Marina's breast during the operation were indeed positive for malignancy, and therefore, as we already knew from Dr. Roth, the tumor was larger than he originally thought. The operation that Marina now needed was a radically modified mastectomy, during which the contents of her entire left breast were removed, except for the skin. The mastectomy had been called "modified" because the pectoral muscles, which were also removed in the past, were now preserved. He also said he planned to examine the affected lymph nodes; a procedure that could have been done during the original surgery. The presence of cancer cells in the lymph nodes determines the main prognostic factor—the presence or absence of metastases that could have spread from the primary breast tumor.

"To be honest, I didn't think your tumor had spread that much," Dr. Keller continued, as dispassionately cool as before. "If I had known then what I know now, I would have asked the radiologist to perform a core needle biopsy of the tumor and a revision of the lymph nodes."

During a core needle biopsy—the standard way to diagnose breast cancer—the doctor removes samples of tissue from various areas in the breast with a hollow needle. A pathologist then studies these tissue samples under a microscope to see if they have cancerous cells.

Marina interrupted him. "But during my first visit, you told us that four and a half centimeters was a large tumor. So, what prevented you from performing a core needle biopsy and examining the lymphatic vessels?"

"It was impossible to predict what the best approach to your surgery was. Each case is different, you know. I operate on breast malignancies daily, and in your case the size of the tumor was borderline after all," Dr. Keller answered, looking past both of us.

We left the surgeon's office very unhappy with what we had just learned. We learned from various sources that a good prognosis of the disease depends on many factors, including the skill and experience of the surgeon. Now we realized that Marina's surgeon, despite his good professional reputation, lacked both. Failure to perform a needle biopsy was an unforgivable omission, due to which Marina needed an added operation. It became clear that it was necessary to look for other, more competent doctors—not only a surgeon but also an oncologist.

Radical Mastectomy at the University Hospital

Our daughter-in-law, Alexandra, a general surgeon, who was always effective in aiding

us with health problems, agreed with Marina's decision that in order to get the best results, she should be treated at a medical center that specialized in breast cancer treatment. That same day, Alexandra contacted her colleague, some of them from her medical residency program to ask for advice. They let her know about Doctor Sorkin, a surgeon with an excellent reputation. He worked at one of the university hospitals in Chicago where he was specializing in breast cancer surgical intervention.

Though it took more than an hour from us to reach the hospital from the suburb where we lived, we were happy to be going to a place where Marina could receive excellent help.

A couple of days later, Dr. Sorkin, in his university office examined Marina and said that before he could come to any conclusions about an approach to her surgery, he must see all her medical records from the community hospital. Having familiarized himself with the available results of earlier studies, he ordered a new mammogram, ultrasound, and MRI scan not of one, but both breasts. From Dr. Sorkin, and later from available literature, once again I was convinced that the quality of the mammography reading is better in the specialized radiological facilities. To my chagrin, I realized then that there was a great possibility that if Marina's annual mammograms had been performed in the specialized mammography department of the university rather than the community hospital, she would have been diagnosed much earlier, thus preventing the primary tumor from potential spread. It turned out that if Marina's tumor had been diagnosed earlier, she might be still alive.

Alas, what's past cannot be redone. As goes the saying, hindsight is 20/20.

Overall, the outcome of Marina's condition possibly would have been better if I had known more about the principles of prevention of breast cancer. For example, with Marina's Jewish descent, I should have taken-- though I still do not know how--more heed to the side effects of her estrogen therapy. According to scientific sources, being of Jewish descent gives a woman a higher probability of having one of the genetic BRCA mutations, which makes her prone to a 50 to 85 percent risk of developing breast cancer by age seventy. Or, if I could turn time back, knowing important factors for a predisposition to breast cancer, I would have insisted on Marina having not only a mammogram but possibly also an ultrasound and an MRI scan on an annual or biannual basis. In addition, there was another subtle point that would justify an aggressive attitude: for at least seven years preceding Marina's diagnosis of breast cancer, she had an unexplained, mild anemia. She had consulted with several hematologists, but nobody could pinpoint the reason for this unresolved prognostic sign. If only I had known what might happen, but, alas, the wheel of fortune cannot be turned back.

In general, contemporary science of medicine is too vast to be sufficiently aware of what is happening in each of its particular field. So, since the time I was involved in the field of oncology, every time I was convinced that I hardly knew about the typical clinical course of breast cancer and about the modern principles of its treatment.

More bad news awaited us during the next visit when Dr. Sorkin let us know that investigation in the university hospital pathology unit established that Marina's cancer was found not in one area of left breast, but it also spread to another focus. In addition to this, it was discovered that she had not ductal, but more aggressive, lobular form of cancer.

As would happen again and again, my wife accepted the bad news stoically, without a single complaint. She never became obsessed with concerns about her health and never lost hope and trust in a good outcome. "My life was well settled before, and I believe it will remain settled one way or another tomorrow as well," she would say. "Whatever happens with me, alike the majority of human beings, I would find way to adapt to changing conditions."

What was important was that she was capable of creating a mental block against thinking what would happen to her in the future; her mind was focused only on the problems of a particular day. "The final destiny of all the living, including me, is the same, so why should I worry about what is awaiting me more than everybody else? *Que sera sera*, what will be will be," she concluded. But the most powerful weapon in the battle with her aggressive cancer was her unfading hope, the key to her unusually long survival. Marina's example taught me that the primary powerful healing force in human life is hope for better.

Based on what Dr. Sorkin told us, we could conclude that previously, general surgeon made at least two big medical errors. Not only that instead of lumpectomy, he should have performed more extensive surgery, a radical mastectomy. Additionally, Dr. Keller had also failed to label the position of the tissues he had removed during the lumpectomy. It was disappointing to know that an allegedly experienced leading surgeon from the community hospital did not follow the established standard of care. Such negligence was inexcusable.

Dr. Sorkin told us that at once after Marina's radical mastectomy, she will be operated by a plastic surgeon, Dr. Belsky. After Dr. Sorkin removes all potentially involved in cancerous process tissue from the involved breast, eventually leaving only a skin bag, the plastic surgeon, will undertake necessary measures to restore the operated breast's cosmetic external appearance to the best of his efforts.

Dr. Belsky examined Marina a week prior to her breast surgery in his office. He told her that procedure that he planned would consist of two phases. The first phase involved remodeling of the involved breast, which could be performed in two ways. The more complicated way was to create a flap consisting of muscular tissue and blood vessels, and when the flap matures, it was supposed to transferred into the involved breast. The other, simpler method consisted of insertion of filled with saline solution silicone prosthesis into the empty skin sack created by radical mastectomy. Based on Marina's age, the long time in surgery for the flap procedure, and the higher rate of complications, without hesitation, Marina chose the silicon prosthesis option. After the described stage of plastic surgery, Dr. Belsky would reduce in size the healthy breast to avoid the emerging cosmetic asymmetry.

On the Day of the Surgery

On the scheduled day for the radical mastectomy, Marina was admitted to the university hospital early in the morning. We said goodbye, kissed each other quickly, and I went to the surgical unit's waiting room.

The well-organized waiting room was managed by two volunteers who treated visitors with respect and understanding. With an anxious heart, I took my seat in the far corner of the room, in vain trying to go through the reading material that I had brought with me. Four hours went by, but the surgery was still not over. Unexpectedly, I felt a light touch on my shoulder. I looked up and saw a friendly face of a middle-aged man wearing a kippah, or yarmulke--the round cloth cap worn by Jewish men according to tradition.

"I was passing by and saw you wear a kippah, which is unusual in my work. So as the hospital chaplain, I decided to approach you. Do you mind?" he asked.

"Quite the opposite. Actually, I am grateful. I would love if you spent a little time with me," I answered. "I do not like to advertise my Jewishness, and usually I do not wear my kippah in public, but as a chaplain, you'll understand why I feel the need to have it on today."

"I understand," the chaplain answered with natural empathy. "For whom are you waiting?"

"Today my wife is having surgery for breast cancer. I have been waiting here for over four hours already," I answered.

"Give me a moment," the chaplain said, and went to the volunteers' desk.

When he returned, he told me that Marina's surgery was over, and she was now in the postoperative area. I would be able to see her when they called me. Saying that, the chaplain took my hand and asked if I would like to tell him my story.

How could I describe what happened just a few words? I politely declined, and once again expressing his sympathy, he took his leave. This encounter, which did not last more than a quarter of an hour, I could never forget. Who could deny that in critical times, any human being is in dire need of words of support and compassion?

A short time after the chaplain left, I looked up and saw before me Dr. Sorkin. Still wearing a surgical gown, he looked exhausted. We shook hands, and he took a seat next to me.

"I just finished long surgery on your wife," he said. "As I expected, your wife's left breast malignancy was quite spread. After the mastectomy, that I performed, Dr. Belsky took over and inserted a prosthesis into the left breast. In addition, to prevent asymmetry of both breasts, I helped Dr. Belsky to reduce the size of her healthy right breast."

Taking a deep breath, he shortly paused. "And now for the unfortunate news. I am sorry, but in your wife's left axillary area, all lymph nodes except one were malignant. According to generally accepted classification, if the cancer spreads to ten or more axillary lymph nodes of the four stages of breast cancer, that means that your wife is in grade IIIC. On the positive side, at least, your wife currently does not have metastases in other parts of her body."

I felt that against my will, tears came to my eyes. For Dr. Sorkin, a surgeon with long experience, who saw much worse situations, my reaction presented nothing new. Nevertheless, he did not ignore my response to bad news.

"You have good reason to be upset with this bad news," he told me in a low, weary voice. "But you should not forget that nowadays oncology has many new and powerful treatment methods, thanks to which this type of cancer can sometimes turn into nothing more than just a chronic disease."

With these words Dr. Sorkin said goodbye, got up, and went about his business. Despite the bad news about Marina's surgical outcome, his words, especially that the cancer might turn into a chronic disease, helped me to regain control over my emotions. I thought that if the outcome of the surgery was not an immediate death sentence, but just foreshadowed a chronic course of her illness, then things are not as bad as they could be. A faint spark of hope flared up in me more and more. The struggle for Marina's life had only started, and I was determined to apply all available means to overcome the tenacious tentacles of cancer. Never give up! I repeated to myself. We will fight.

It was not news for me that "hope" is a magic word. I discovered that if there is still hope then everything is possible. Even in the most critical medical situations, hope helps maintain the sanity of mind and spirit. Hope prevents people to take their life; it is an inexhaustible source of faith in the future. Even for the most sober and objective of minds, hope provides impetus to go forward and courageously fight an insidious enemy that could hide inside of one's own body. At this most dramatic moment in my life, I still didn't know how in the future the magic word "hope" would help both Marina and me to move forward on our new, difficult path of life.

After two uneventful days in the hospital, Marina was discharged home. Though she knew the truth about the results of the surgery, she remained strong and undaunted. Nothing in her appearance portrayed fear or anxiety, and this unshakable resolve would never abandon her in the future. For many years afterward, I was constantly amazed by my wife's brave and fearless reaction to an incessant, continuous stream of bad news. If this was not heroism, what else could it be?

Over the long period of Marina's illness, there were times I could not resist asking her the source of her courage and spiritual strength in the face of the relentless and gradual progression of her cancer, when one organ after another of her body was yielding to the invasion by malignant cells.

"I must tell you that though you are a smart and grown-up guy, you still do not understand simple truths," Marina once responded in a voice devoid of any sign of drama. "Listen, I'm not a sophisticated a woman as you might think. I take life as it is. Today I feel normal, and it is enough for me to be happy. Why should I look forward, if even a healthy person cannot be sure they will survive until tomorrow?"

Marina did not like to exaggerate her problems. Perceiving her current condition as nothing unusual, she was doing her best to be treated as a healthy person, and she never tried to evoke sympathy toward herself, including those who were part of a close family. When I asked her why she did not tell the truth about her condition when our friends inquired her, her typical answer was "Why complain? It will not make me feel any better. As long as I have you and my children, I do not need condolences."

Oncologist Dr. Genovesi and the First-Line Therapy

Three days after the surgery, Marina had her first appointment with her oncologist, Dr. Genovesi, a member of the university hospital's oncological medical group. When we were invited into an examining room, Marina was first examined by a medical student, after which in the exam room entered Dr. Genovesi, a middle-aged woman, slightly plump and energetic. She was accompanied by a fellow in oncology, a resident, and the medical student who just examined Marina. Dr. Genovesi was professional and effective, but like many other doctors in her profession, her manner being formal, she treated Marina as if the patient belonged to a different dimension of life than her physician. It appeared to me that the patients belonged to the category of the sick, possibly dying people, while she, alive and well, belonged to the category where people lived in Shangri-la.

To the moment of the appointment, Dr. Genovesi already had medical records about Marina's earlier health history. Among many other questions, she asked Marina if she had ever taken estrogen preparations. When the oncologist received a positive answer from Marina, she exchanged, as it appeared to me, knowing glances with the other members of her team, which at once alarmed me. While Dr. Genovesi was performing the physical examination, silence reigned in the room. At the end of the visit, she ordered blood tests and told Marina that she should come for a follow-up visit in a week, when her chemotherapy treatment was planned to start.

From Dr. Genovesi, we learned that the treatment of majority oncological conditions is based on existing national protocols. Guided by these protocols, the doctor chooses drug or drug combinations most effective in the treatment of a particular type of a malignant disease. However, medicine is not only a science, but also an art, and people are not robots. Each human being presents a unique genetic makeup, and this behooves the doctor to tailor the existing protocol to individual case. Indeed, without an appreciation of individuality it is difficult to treat many diseases.

It is logical to assume that oncologists are drawn to their specialty not only for its medical complexity, but also as an opportunity for deep emotional connection with the patients and their families. Those oncologists who integrate medical knowledge with professional intuition have a valuable experience in customizing treatment to a particular situation. They are prepared to deal with clinically ambiguous cases and to manage complications resulting from the disease and from the intense treatment of patients' health conditions. From years of experience, they learn how to meet difficult challenges and how to psychologically deal with the patients and caregivers in a time of vast uncertainty.

The complexity of the management of many types of cancer is the reason why some patients and their caregivers--mostly by word of mouth-- are looking for "the most experienced doctors" and for the best medical facilities. Looking backward, I am convinced that after being diagnosed with breast cancer, Marina would not have survived for thirteen whole years if she continued to be treated in the community hospital, where the specialists clearly did not have as much experience as their colleagues in the specialized and advanced facility, notwithstanding a lack of the most advanced technical equipment.

Like most other patients, during our visits to different oncologists, Marina and I asked them what her prognosis was. We quickly learned the way oncologists answer such question. Unless they stay silent, their standard response is something like, "Well, it is difficult to make such a prediction right now, let's wait and see . . ." If after that, unsatisfied patients, in a voice choking with anxiety, continue their inquiry and ask something like, "Is it a month, half a year, a year or longer, doctor?" This time, the oncologist's next answer is even more vague. To ask more questions after such an exchange is useless. The doctor will just repeat the same answer but in a different way because, in the first place, frequently the oncologists themselves do not know what the clinical response to the treatment will be for a particular patient. The course of a cancer depends on many factors, and the main factor of it depends on the unique genetics of the individual and therefore this course might be totally unpredictable.

Be as it may, when during our first visit to Dr. Genovesi, she gave us a vague response, with Marina's silent permission, not stopping my inquiry, I insisted on a more precise answer.

"Well, okay, since you are so persistent in your inquiry," Dr. Genovesi said reluctantly, "I will give you this answer. In your wife's case, it is between six months to . . . let's say five years."

"Fifteen!" burst out of my mouth at this moment against my will. I threw this out in a low voice, and nobody paid attention to my remark, but as God is my witness, I never knew my words would become prophetic.

Leaving the examining room, we returned to the waiting room, where I took a seat while Marina went to the reception desk to schedule the blood tests for the next appointment. Sitting there and recollecting what just happened during the visit, I recalled the unpleasant, as it appeared to me, expression on Dr. Genovesi' s face when Marina told her that she had been taking estrogen for several years. Suddenly, a powerful wave of guilt overwhelmed me. I decided that it was my fault that I, a physician by profession, had not been able to find an alternative to hormone replacement therapy for my wife's hot flashes. Marina would not have had breast cancer, I thought, if she had not taken those estrogen preparations. The sense of guilt was so strong that something very unusual happened to me: I started to silently sob, tears flowing from my eyes.

"What's the matter with you?" Marina asked me sternly when she returned from the receptionist. Courageous by nature, she hardly ever cried, and she hated seeing me, her reliable support, weeping. Since the day we met, right or wrong, for better or for worse, she saw in me a strong and courageous man, and she refused to part with this view.

After I explained to her the reason for my reaction, she once more ordered me strictly to stop sobbing and to calm down. "Now listen what I tell you, Vovka," she said, looking at me sternly. "Countless times I heard from different sources that taking estrogen might be dangerous. How could you forget that following your own advice, on numerous occasions, I tried to replace estrogen with something different, but nothing helped? You should understand once and for all that without estrogen, I simply would not have been able to function for all these long years. Hormone replacement therapy literally helped me to survive, and without it, I would not have been able to continue to work and function at home. It is my body, and it was my own decision. Better wipe your face, and never cry—I repeat, never cry—in my presence ever again. I hate when you, my man, cry, and don't dare to do it anymore. Never forget that I have my own will, and the final decisions that concern me belong to me until I am gone."

Around that time, Dr. Genovesi, came up to us. She was alerted by the receptionist who from her desk could see my reaction. Instead of her previously formal and impassive manner, before us now stood a caring and warm human being. She reminded me that hormone replacement therapy is the standard treatment and that millions of women suffering from severe hot flashes take hormones daily. "Do not exaggerate the problem. If you had read the literature more carefully, you would have seen that 6.3 percent of women who have never used estrogen replacement develop invasive breast cancer, while the chances for women who have used the hormone replacement therapy for five years is 8.3 percent. That's roughly one extra cancer diagnosis for every fifty users."

I felt ashamed that I stole the attention from Marina, who deserved it infinitely more than I did. How could I forget that it was Marina who had cancer, not me? I should be her support, strong and unshakable. As her husband and best friend, it was my responsibility to help her to never lose hope. With that thought, I pulled myself together and thanked Dr. Genovesi.

Before leaving the clinic, we called our son and his wife and told them what had happened at the appointment. While Marina was talking on the phone, my overriding thought was, that blessed are those lucky enough to have close family for which the health and destiny of their dear one is close to their hearts. It is one thing to hear words of sympathy and encouragement from friends and acquaintances, but another to hear such words from those who have a quality of a genuine love.

On the way home, Marina reminded me that blaming anyone, including myself, was a road to nowhere. I knew she was right. She never blamed herself or anyone else for her problems.

As usual, Marina's visit to the treatment area for her first-line chemotherapy was preceded by blood tests. By the time she was called in for treatment, the blood test results were ready. If the count of white blood cells, red blood cells, platelets, or other components of her blood was lower or higher than acceptable, the doctor might postpone the current appointment. The postponement could last a week or more. When necessary, the patients could receive a medication that stimulated the production of the specific blood component that was compromised. In Marina's case, on several occasions, it was necessary to increase her white blood cell count, and correspondingly she received a white blood cell booster called Neulasta.

As former immigrants from the Soviet Union, both of us were happy that here in the USA, Marina had a chance to be treated with the best methods of modern medicine.

I had my own history of experience with the wonders of American medicine. After my family had arrived in the United States from Russia and I had passed medical exams necessary in order to practice in the USA, starting in 1975, I worked as a pediatric resident at Illinois Masonic Hospital in Chicago. My first clinical rotation there happened to be on the neonatal ICU floor. The first day of my rotation there can be attributed to the category of unforgettable events. When I showed up at the nursery floor in the early morning and saw the medical equipment there, I felt as if I had just arrived from another planet. In the Soviet Union at that time, the equipment used to monitor and treat sick newborns, if it was available, was primitive by world standards. In the nursery at Illinois Masonic Hospital, for the first time in my professional life, I saw enclosed cribs—Isolettes—supplied with all that was necessary to support a newborn's life. It may be hard to understand, but I simply could not believe that disposable medical equipment could exist. For me it was such a colossal waste because in the Soviet Union, at that time, needles, syringes, and diapers would be reused countless times until they were completely worn out. For the first time in my life, I saw incubators and Isolettes provided with oxygen and vacuums, cardiac monitors, and instruments for manipulation on umbilical vessels, all of which were disposable. As a pediatrician with ten years of experience behind me, I was amazed when for the first time, I learned of the existence of such essential nutritional items as baby formula. I had read about some of these things in scientific journals, but I never dreamed that I would be seeing them during my lifetime. I felt as though I had been magically transported to the next century, which actually was true.

Now, thirty years later, in the oncological department, where I sat and waited for Marina, I could not help but be surprised by the medical diagnostic and treatment equipment used daily for patients with complicated health challenges and conditions. For the umpteenth time, I saw the impressive development of medical science, never ceasing in its search for new, more effective means to treat and eradicate different malignancies.

Driven by the desire to reduce the patients' stress during their stay in the waiting and treatment areas, the hospital founders showed true generosity and ingenuity. Numerous details of the furnishings such as the armchairs, carpets, and pictures on the walls were all of high quality. Volunteers in the waiting area offered patients and their caregivers or family members crackers and drinks of different kinds. This and other tokens of respect for the patients created a spirit of humanity to the could-be sterile medical environment and emphasized the human dignity of the patients with any income who were forced to deal with their illnesses. A thoughtful interior lifted the spirit, reassuring visitors that they were surrounded by the compassionate care of empathetic health care providers.

I wish I knew selection methods for hiring personnel for the oncological center. I had an opportunity to see it then and later that overwhelming number of those who worked there were not only highly trained professionals but also human beings who were sincerely compassionate toward their patients. They had the natural ability to console patients who were burdened with chronic and often incurable diseases.

Though the daily life of oncological patients was poisoned by the knowledge that they had a severe disease, as a rule, their external appearances did not betray what was in their minds. Looking at the cancer victims of all ages who were in the waiting room, some of whom were tragically young, some mature and old, most of the time it was impossible to figure out which of the patients had a mild case and which had a severe case of dreadful disease. The exceptions were patients who were forced to be wheelchair bound, those who had noticeable hair loss, and those who were visibly exhausted by their condition.

"You see, Vovka, how lucky I am, that I am to have my cancer in my older age," Marina, an incurable optimist, would tell me repeatedly. "Until now, I have lived a long and happy life but look at those beautiful young women. When I see them, my heart aches for them, and I feel terrible that they must go through their illness so young. Many of them have children. I hope they get well, but who can replace a parent to their children in the case of a tragic outcome? The ways of God are so incomprehensible."

According to statistics, single adults in the USA accounted for over 45 percent of the US population. Nevertheless, overwhelming majority of the patients who visited the oncological center were accompanied by one or more support individuals. It was either a spouse, a boyfriend or girlfriend, parents, relatives, neighbors, or friends. On many occasions, I saw relatively grown-up children who accompanied their parents or grandparents.

Fortunately, in any situation involving bad news, there is also "not-so bad news." With all the bad news of the past weeks, there was a silver lining in the dark cloud. Before Marina started her chemo, we were informed that her previous diagnostic test showed that her type of cancer was estrogen and progesterone positive, which--according to statistical data--meant that she had a better chance of long-term survival.

Initially, Dr. Genovesi prescribed a typical first-line therapy regimen for the treatment of Marina's stage of metastatic breast cancer. The combination, known as an FEC combination, consisted of 5-Fluoracil, Epirubicin, and Cyclophosphamide intravenous therapy. After weeks of treatment with the FEC combination were over, she was prescribed intravenous infusions of Taxotere.

Classified as a plant alkaloid, Taxotere is an anticancer chemotherapy drug, and Marina was supposed to receive six cycles of it, given every other week. The first three doses she tolerated well, but then she developed severe fatigue, loss of appetite, and dehydration. Energetic and unaffected before she began to receive chemotherapy, now she became weak and sick. On the third day of her suffering, we decided she must be hospitalized. When we left the house, she was so sick that she was hardly able to walk to the car without my support.

At the end of visit to the emergency room of the university hospital, Marina was hospitalized for treatment of her dehydration. In the hospital, she received intravenous fluids, and already on the second day of treatment, her condition improved enough to be discharged home. Once again, I could see that infusion of intravenous fluids was one of the greatest achievements in medicine. Over the past hundred years, it has helped to save countless human lives worldwide.

After two days of hospital treatment, Marina went home and Taxotere treatment resumed.

Vasomotor Hot Flashes Do Not Subside

Unfortunately, Marina's chemotherapy treatment worsened her hot flashes. At the very beginning of chemotherapy, to control this unpleasant symptom, which now was contraindicated to be controlled with estrogen, Dr. Genovesi prescribed the antidepressant psychotropic medication Effexor. The doctor assured Marina that this drug had helped many of her patients who suffered from hot flashes. She expected that Marina would benefit from it as well. Alas, the oncologist's predictions did not come to pass. Effexor and other psychotropic medications she tried did not agree with Marina. Instead of helping her, it influenced her mental state badly, making her depressed and, to some degree, confused. Not losing hope of controlling the nagging symptom, Marina and I explored the possibility of using different folk remedies, hoping it might help. However, even before she started to take the alternative treatment, we learned that practically all folk remedies contain natural estrogen-like hormonal properties, which made them contraindicated and useless in treating hot flashes. Eventually, Marina did not have any other choice than to bite the bullet. Day in and day out, courageously and patiently, she went through numerous episodes of hot flashes. Thanks to what I could see, I realized that countless women who are prone to hot flashes deserve a lot of respect and compassion for their stoic acceptance of this serious discomfort.

During the time when Marina was getting her treatment for cancer, she still worked at CNA, the large insurance company located in the famous large red building that decorates downtown Chicago. Her managers did their best to accommodate her medical needs and allowed her to have appointments at the university hospital during her working hours. She never forgot to give the company back one or two hours of her time by leaving later in the day.

Treatment Has Side Effects. The Barber's Tears

Despite the intensive chemotherapy, in general, Marina tolerated her treatment well, thanks not only to her good general health and relatively young age of sixty-two but also because of availability of different precious medications to treat her symptoms. We are lucky we live in a time when modern medicine offers patients quite effective remedies to handle annoying side effects from chemotherapy such as fatigue, nausea, diarrhea, and loss of appetite. Steroids helped Marina to fight the inflammatory reactions produced by chemo; other valuable drugs helped her to deal with loss of appetite and other unpleasant symptoms. As for fatigue, generally speaking, Marina's was not so bad as to require special treatment for it.

Hair loss is one of unavoidable symptom during chemotherapy. Three weeks after starting her primary chemo treatment, Marina's hair began to fall out in clumps. As soon as she noticed hair on her pillow and in her comb, without hesitation, she decided to have her hair cut.

Anticipating the possible reaction from her hairdresser and other members of the beauty salon she usually visited, Marina hesitated to go to her usual place. Noticing her reluctance, I suggested she could go to the barbershop where I had been going for a long time. In this barbershop worked three barbers. All of them were Italian.

When we got to the barbershop, the master who usually cut my hair was not there, and the only barber who was available that day was George, a man in his mid-seventies. Whenever I had seen him before at the barbershop, he was lost in deep thought. My impression was that he did not notice me, although without looking at me, he would not hesitate to answer my greeting. It was a men's barbershop, but because I was a regular customer, they agreed to take care of Marina. When the next barber's chair became vacant, Marina took a seat on it. Approaching her, George, in a low voice, asked what kind of haircut she wanted. Marina calmly answered that she wanted him to cut off all her hair completely. The old barber visibly froze for a moment when she finished her request.

"Why do you want to cut off your hair, Miss?" George asked Marina in his pleasant voice, not hiding his disbelief in what he had just heard. "To me your hair looks pretty good, Miss. Why do you want to be bald?"

"I just received three weeks of chemotherapy for cancer," Marina answered, without a hint of a drama in her voice, "and now my hair has begun to fall out. That's why, sir."

Giving Marina a long look, George knowingly nodded his gray-haired head, and set to work. While he was cutting her hair, I became engrossed in reading a medical magazine I had brought with me. Finishing a small article, I looked up and noticed that George was almost done with cutting Marina's hair. Then I saw something that is impossible to forget. While George, this reserved old man of few words, was finishing his barber work, I saw stream of tears, yes, real tears, flowing down his cheeks. *What's Hecuba to him, or he to*

Hecuba? Who was Marina to him? Another client, nothing more. But before me was another angel, one of those kind human souls I would meet many times on Marina's path in her fight with the wicked cancer. If not for what had happened that day, I never would have known what a kind heart beats in the chest of this old man whom I never suspected to be such a sensitive and compassionate person. Yes, human beings could not be judged by their appearance.

Hair Care as a Common Cause

During one of the next visits to the oncology center, at the time bald-headed Marina was surprised when her attending physician told her that it was time for her to visit the university hospital hair center.

"Are you sure?" Marina asked, "I doubt any hair specialist can help me as long as I am on chemotherapy."

The attending physician smiled knowingly and told Marina that before jumping to conclusions, she should visit a hair specialist at the university.

The staff of the hair center, who helped women, consisted of three volunteers, all females, all of them cancer survivors. The patients who were going through the emotional trauma of temporary or permanent hair loss received service in the hair center regardless of their financial status. Entire hair replacement inventory was donated to the center free of charge by outside private companies, and by individual donors. The main contributors were manufacturers of the hair merchandise. The main things provided to the clients were wigs of various kinds made of either human or artificial hair, plus hairpieces and other cosmetic devices related to hair loss. Women devastated by cancer could appreciate the cost-free wigs, but even more they appreciated the evidence that they were not forgotten, that trauma related to their illness was acknowledged by the community at large, and that around them were people full of desire to help in their trying times.

The hair center consisted of two rooms. A hospitable and friendly woman in her senior years, the hair center volunteer, warmly greeted us when we arrived. The volunteer invited us into the front room, invited Marina to take a seat, and then placed in front of her a medium-sized mirror. Then from another room, she brought a bunch of wigs and hairpieces, which might be also called toupees. By this time, Marina's remaining hair was growing on the periphery of her scalp, so by covering mostly the top of her head, the wig with artificial semi-gray hair, that she chose, fit her well. Among the other items Marina received in the hair center was also a hairpiece, a small section of real or artificial hair that is intended to cover small areas of the scalp lacking hair. Usually, hairpiece is worn to cover a bald spot or to make hair look longer, thicker, or of a different color.

We left the center in a half an hour. During this pleasant visit, I learned that an industry exists that had been unknown to me, dedicated to helping people--in this case mostly to the women who suffered from hair loss from different reasons.

Marina had always enjoyed driving, and whenever she was not tired, she insisted to be in charge of the car. Ability to drive was very important for her. It was not only because she loved to drive, but because each time it proved to her that she was independent, that she was still in a satisfactory physical shape, and that she could still take care of herself. Driving our car on the way to home from the visit to the hair center, in the middle of the trip, Marina who drove the car, for a second, turned to me and said, "How happy I am that we live in this incredible country, Vovka. Only imagine, though I am no one else than one of countless cancer sufferers in this country, there are people for whom I am not indifferent and invisible, who want to help me. Great is the country where we live, a country that does not ignore those who live through the time when they need sympathy and help."

Caring for the Heart Muscle

For most breast cancer patients, the risk of developing heart failure from chemotherapy and radiation therapy is relatively low. However, many women need to receive numerous courses of chemotherapy lasting for many years and in this case low annual risk adds up to a higher cumulative risk. That's why a MUGA scan—a multigated acquisition scan, a noninvasive diagnostic test used to evaluate the pumping function of the ventricles—was ordered for Marina. In a MUGA scan, a small amount of radioactive tracer is injected into a vein, and a special camera then takes images of the beating heart. Fortunately, this study showed that Marina's heart is normal, thanks to which she received numerous chemotherapy treatments without cardiac complications in the future.

The First Venous Access Port

Marina's superficial veins appeared to be in good shape. They were visible, palpable, and easily available for numerous injections. However, everything eventually comes to an end, and after several months of intense use, the veins became difficult to access for the injections. Mainly, those who had compromised her veins were not the nurses, all of whom were excellently manipulating veins, but the medical technicians of the different diagnostic imaging departments. While some of them were good at it, there were many who either did not have adequate skills or who did not take this procedure seriously. Eventually, when it became impossible to find satisfactory patent veins, her oncologist suggested that Marina should have a venous access port installed for her. A venous access port is a small medical appliance that is placed beneath the skin. A vein connects the port with a catheter, which serves as a site for intravenous injection. As done in the most cases, Marina's port was inserted in the upper chest just below the clavicle or collarbone, leaving her arms free from injections. A venous access port is not always ideal, but the problems with it are far less than the burden of multiple traumatic punctures to the veins. Marina was happy to receive the port, which safeguarded her from many episodes of pain during venipunctures for all kinds of purposes.

Treatment Partner. Singing While Waiting for the Elevator

In Marina's presence, I did my best to keep my worries hidden from her. She hardly ever expressed fears or concerns, and it was invariably I, her husband in good health, who was more nervous and stressed about whatever was going on with her. She would complain about minor things such as pain and discomfort, but she avoided discussions of the most important problems with her heath.

There is a mountain of books written about the suffering of those who have a serious illness, but along with them affected and suffer deeply are the caregivers, those dedicated people who take care of their afflicted dear ones. The availability of a reliable caregiver—a caregiver who really cares, who is attached to the patient with the invisible threads of love and commitment, and who stays informed about the patient's illness--is one of the cornerstones in extending the life of the patient. When outsiders are expressing sympathy to the seriously sick person, they hardly ever think about the role of the caregiver who is providing for the many needs of the patient. There are many reasons of concern and worries for those who are devoted to the patient. Dedicated caregivers might experience not only physical exhaustion but also constant emotional pain and anxiety related to the well-being of their loved one. In my case, like countless caregivers before and after me, I could not stop worrying about the health of my best friend.

Over time, I developed different techniques that helped me to reduce my chronic painful worry about Marina's well-being. One of such techniques was to sing my favorite songs and melodies in English and Russian. Without a doubt, while no psychotropic medicine could help me in this situation, the melodies I'd known from childhood usually produced a magical soothing effect. No wonder many schools around the world have a special singing lesson. Depending on the circumstances, sometimes I sang familiar tunes to myself; sometimes I was humming in an undertone, and sometimes, when no one was around me, I sang them aloud.

One day, when Marina and I were leaving from an appointment where the oncologist had told her about newly discovered metastases in her liver, we stood in front of an elevator's door on the way down to the hospital lobby. Not realizing what I was doing to calm myself after another load of bad news, I sang in undertone, but it turned out loud enough for people around me to hear me. It was not me, but my subconscious mind, by itself, that chose the song fitting for the moment. The words of the song I was humming were from the musical *Phantom of the Opera* by Andrew Lloyd Weber. "In sleep he sang to me, in dreams he came / That voice which calls to me and speaks my name . . ."

I think Marina never suspected the reason for my way of singing. Unaware that a couple had joined us in waiting for the slow elevator, I continued humming to myself. Overwhelmed with dark thoughts, understanding that somebody was addressing me, I paused my humming. I looked up and saw an African American man in his mid-fifties who stood next to a White woman, most possibly his wife. On the face of this man shone a kind and cordial smile, a smile that better than many words expressed his sincere humane feelings.

"Nice melody you sing," he said, not taking from me his sharp gaze, "I understand you. Yes, my friend, sometimes life is not a bowl of cherries, but we do not have any other choice but to go forward. I also sing when things are not going my way."

It is not possible to know what is going on in another human's mind. But among us there are caring angels like the one who had just spoken to me. His few unforgettable words meant more to me than any sedative. "*Доброе слово и кошке приятно*," which in English could be translated as "At a kind word, even a cat is pleased," is a relevant Russian expression for such an occasion.

Radiation Treatment

When Marina was done with her first intense course of chemotherapy, she was scheduled for the course of radiation treatment. Before the treatment started, Dr. Belsky, the plastic surgeon, with the help of a syringe, infused saline solution into the prosthesis, extending it in width to the maximal degree.

Also prior to radiation treatment, Marina had a localization system procedure, during which the radiation oncologist created a "map" to deliver the prescribed doses of radiation with maximal precision by placing two dot tattoo marks on her chest. Afterward she received external radiation to her breast and lymph node areas once a day, five days a week, for seven weeks.

The localization system allowed focused and precise targeting and tracking in order to supply radiation only to the affected area, thereby reducing radiation exposure to minimum to the nearby healthy tissues of the heart, lungs, and other organs. For her radiation treatments, she was able to drive to the university hospital on her own during her work hours.

From the beginning, the entire course of Marina's treatment did not prevent her from working full-time at her job. Much credit goes to the supportive managers of the CNA corporation she worked for, who did their best to help her to keep her full-time status.

First-Line Therapy Is Over. Hope for Recovery

The entire course of first-line therapy, which consisted of extensive surgery, chemo, and radiation therapy, Marina tolerated well. During radiation, the moderate pain and redness of her skin were soothed by creams and ointments. A more serious side effect was fatigue, which lasted about a month and then gradually disappeared. Even during the most difficult period of her treatment, her enthusiastic and unarguable "Perfect!" was the only answer that our friends got from her when they inquired her how she felt.

When Marina was done with her radiotherapy, her oncologist prescribed a maintenance medication, Arimidex, which belongs to a class of medications called nonsteroidal aromatase inhibitors. Research has proved that increased concentrations of circulating estrogens are strongly associated with increased risk for breast cancer, especially in postmenopausal women. Arimidex works by decreasing the amount of estrogen the body makes.

The aggressive course of treatment for Marina's metastatic cancer was finished in 2005, and then she entered a symptom-free stage of cancer, professionally called a "no evidence of disease stage." Since then, her visits to the university hospital reduced to twice a year.

Eventually Marina's health fully improved, and she returned to her normal self. She continued to work full-time, and she liked it. Other than the daily intake of her prescribed antihormonal Arimidex medication, there were no lingering reminders of the nightmare of recent events. As in the good old days, we enjoyed visiting our children and our friends, attended parties, went hiking, and traveled. I enjoyed watching Marina eat eagerly. We did everything that creative, normal people would do in our place. However, behind this illusory denial of the recent past, on a more sober level, we never forgot that metastatic cancer remained an uninvited guest in our family, which did not turn Marina into a hypochondriac—just the opposite. Our biggest rule was not to let negative thoughts prevail, and we both never lost undying hope for future good times.

Back in 1966, when I was a young boy, I'd had a chance to watch a popular Swedish movie *A Princess*. It was a romantic movie where a beautiful young bride who was diagnosed with a dreadful case of cancer courageously fought the fatal disease and eventually fully recovered. At the end of the movie, she and her groom celebrate her wonderful recovery, to the joy and tears of naïve viewers like me.

Maybe this movie was a fairy tale, or--who knows--it might have been true. In any case, I passionately wanted to believe--and it was surprisingly easy--that against all the odds, the same miracle would occur with Marina. And why not? Wasn't our meeting on the beach of the Black Sea a real miracle? Was it not a miracle that we were able to pass successfully through the Soviet Union's iron curtain to freedom in 1974? There were other undoubted miracles in our lives, for example, my successful improvement and good health after the quintuple-bypass cardiac surgery that I had in 1995, and that my son has a wonderful family. If all these miracles were possible then why should I not expect that another miracle was possible, and my Marina would also be able to triumph against her nasty prognosis? Haven't we all heard or read about cases where a person sentenced to death with inoperable cancer recovered? Who knows, maybe Marina would also enjoy a miraculous recovery. Against all the odds, consciously and subconsciously, I sincerely believed it would happen. She surely deserved such a miracle. I can confess that, despite all my education and my skeptical mind, in the current situation, a part of me believed in miracles, and I sincerely believed that Marina would escape the premature tragic outcome from her menacing disease. I prayed it would happen.

CHAPTER 3

Respite from Fate

The Road to Hope

Our charming granddaughter Ruth, or Ruthie, was born in 2002 when our son and his wife lived in Milwaukee, a city located approximately at a ninety-minute drive from Chicago. When a babysitter was necessary to take care of our granddaughter, Marina was always glad to offer her help. Taking care of Ruthie was not a job for her but a pleasure. Sometimes with me, but more often by herself, she drove from Chicago to Milwaukee and spent a day or more there looking after our little granddaughter. At all times, then and for many years afterward, taking care of Ruthie and later of our grandson, Ariel, who was born two years later, always produced a healing effect on babysitter Grandma Marina.

After Marina's initial chemotherapy in 2005 and 2006, her general health and blood tests were within normal limits all the time. She felt good, her spirits were as high as they'd been before she was diagnosed with cancer, and she performed all our domestic chores. In 2006, her oncologist, Dr. Genovesi, left the university; so during the following years while Marina was symptom free, different fellows in oncology in the university clinic took care of her visits. A fellow is a fully credentialed physician who has completed their residency and is completing further training in a specialty. Before these examinations, she would have a blood test taken by a lab technician. When the results of the test were ready, she was examined by one of the fellows, whose routine consisted of a minute of listening to Marina's chest and less than a minute of palpating the abdomen, then looking at the computer for the results of the blood test. At the conclusion of the short visit, the doctor would shortly tell Marina that everything was well with her health, and that for next visit, she should come six months later.

As a physician, I understood that such a superficial examination could be justified considering the state of remission of Marina's disease. As long as she did not complain about anything, it was not expected to find anything abnormal during her exam. My wife's remission, or as it called in medical lexicon "no evidence of disease," lasted for seven years, from 2005 to 2012. During this time, Marina and I, two clearly naïve people, wanted to believe that the cancer had entered a hibernation stage and possibly even gone away. We ignored the simple fact that in order to come to such a definitive conclusion, imaging studies such as an MRI, CT scan, plain X-rays, and bone scans needed to be performed.

In hopes of Marina's complete recovery, we drove to her regular semiannual visits along the same stretch of road leading toward the hospital, which we dubbed the Road of Hope.

As we learned later, following the initial treatment, the standard approach toward breast cancer is a hands-off attitude toward any further intervention until the patient develops symptoms based on a clinical evaluation. That standard is not applicable to some other forms of cancer, such as rectal cancer. But in the case of breast cancer, it has been proven by research studies that it is better to not resume treatment unless or until the patient's breast cancer raises its head again.

Nobody ever explained to us about such an approach, and that's why already after the fourth uneventful visit, as a true optimist, Marina asked me on the way home, if she felt so excellent and did not have any symptoms, why she needed to go for the next appointment at all. Not being informed about the accepted approach to the management of breast cancer in the stage she was on, I could not answer her question and told her that she should rely on her doctor's recommendation. This seven-year-long misunderstanding would not have existed if just one of the physicians who examined Marina had told us where she belonged in the overall timetable of the disease. If we, two educated people, suffered from such naivete, what about the less-educated patients? What prevented our healers from taking a minute or two to explain to us what was going on instead of assuming we knew about something that was so foreign to us and obvious to them?

Oncologist Dr. Arnold

In the summer of 2008, at one of the local hospitals where I was on staff, I attended a continuing education lecture. This time it was a lecture on advances in the treatment of breast cancer. The lecturer, Dr. Myra Arnold, a middle-aged woman, who was one of the university's leading clinical oncologists with remarkable teaching and research credentials, impressed me with her deep knowledge of the subject. At the end of the lecture, I approached her and briefly told her about Marina's illness. Dr. Arnold listened to me attentively and at the end of the conversation kindly agreed to be Marina's attending physician.

Two weeks later, Marina had an appointment with Dr. Arnold. The treatment center for her medical group was comfortable, with proper attention provided to the details of each patient's needs. In addition to the center's generous decor, it had a spectacular outside view. The center's designers followed the proven principle that fulfilling the spiritual needs of patients resulted in better outcomes. The administration's aim was to create a pleasing and friendly environment for the patients. They did it out of respect for the people who were attending the center. Their endeavors were generously supported by wealthy benefactors and small donors from the community at large. The staff of the center was outstanding in their sincere desire to let the patients know that they had come to the right place in their search for excellent care. Thus, in this difficult time of their lives, patients were reassured that they were at treatment center where they were respected and where they would be well cared for.

The main goal of our visit was to hear from Marina's new doctor more elaborate explanation of Marina's current condition. Shortly after a nurse took Marina's vital signs, one of the department's fellows, but not Dr. Arnold, entered the examining room. Seeing the fellow, Marina in a quiet but firm voice told her that today she wanted to see Dr. Arnold. It was probably not the first time the fellow had found herself in a similar situation, so she nodded her head knowingly and left the room, promising Marina that her doctor would be coming soon. Indeed, a short time later, the door opened, and Dr. Myra Arnold entered. Of her dignified appearance, the most remarkable features were her thoughtful dark eyes and shiny, raven-black hair. She was attentive and respectful while Marina described the history of her illness. When Marina finished, doctor asked her several questions.

The physical examination performed by Dr. Arnold was as superficial as the ones performed by the fellows in the past. Based on my personal experience and observations, I understood that the majority of contemporary physicians relied not so much on the result of physical exam as on results of the lab and imaging tests. Thus, it turned out that lately physical exam performed doctors mostly is short in duration, and patients are mostly examined without taking off their clothes. As a rule, prior to the visit, blood pressure is taken without raising a patient's sleeve. The weight of the patient, required by insurance company protocols, mostly is taken the same way in different seasons of the year. In the cold season, it might be taken with heavy shoes or without them, with a heavy coat or without it. Since the weight might differ significantly from visit to visit depending how it was taken, obviously the doctors are not interested too much in the real weight of the patient.

In our new doctor we liked that despite the age of ubiquitous technology during the visit, she used her computer only in order to look up Marina's medical history; as for the progress note of the visit, she entered it in her computer later in her office. Her approach allowed Dr. Arnold to keep good eye contact with us during the exam. In conclusion of the visit, she told us that presently she did not see anything abnormal in condition of Marina's health and that she would see her in half of a year, or earlier, if Marina developed unusual symptoms.

CHAPTER 4

And Again, the Storm

A Suspicious Cough

Marina's cancer did not raise its ugly face high enough for seven whole years--a long time for her primarily diagnosed advanced stage of metastatic cancer. Dreams, sweet dreams! During this long span of time, seeing her impressive energy, I naïvely did not stop hoping that her cancer would just fade away from her body. As for Marina, she never wanted to talk about her disease. She had a mental mechanism that turned her thoughts away from such unpleasant things. Though she was endowed with a great critical mind, by nature, she did not want to think about things that were out of her control. We hardly ever discussed her condition and behaved as if nothing was happening with her health.

In April 2012, seven years after Marina's first treatment of breast cancer, she was sixty-nine, we visited our friends in Bonita Springs, Florida. We stayed in a nice hotel located in a fabulously beautiful area where flowering plants and splendid tropical colorful vegetation grew and bloomed year-round. Every day we took long walks in this paradise of a place. Marina was more energetic than I was, and as always, she overtook me at the beginning of our strolls. Enjoying our pastime too much to rush, I periodically asked her to slow down. That was when I suddenly realized that there was an annoyance that was spoiling our activity. It turned out that the peaceful walk was being disturbed by Marina's persistent dry, nonproductive cough. Listening to it, I recalled that I'd heard this dry cough several days earlier, but then her cough had been episodic, while now it was persistent. When I asked her for the reason of her cough, she only shrugged and waved a hand. Eventually, when I repeated my question, she gave me her disarming smile and told me earnestly to leave her alone since the cough did not bother her at all.

"Why worry?" she added. "Nonsense. Who knows why I am coughing? I probably have a small upper respiratory infection. What else, do you think?"

How could it be a symptom of respiratory infection, I thought to myself, if she does not have any other symptoms of it?

Three days later, we returned to Chicago. The next day, it was Saturday, Marina's condition with cough had improved to such a degree that we went to a religious service at our synagogue, a place where, as always, we had a good time.

When the service was over, Marina followed me through a narrow alley walking to our car. Reaching the sidewalk, I turned around and saw her standing near a low pole at the mouth of the alley, trying to push aside a hanging loose metal sign "No Left Turn," trying to prevent this sign from scratching a car that was just leaving the alley. Unfortunately, the driver of the car was poorly coordinated ninety-four-year-old synagogue parishioner. On top of it, that day this parishioner forgot his glasses at home and was driving too close to the protruding sign. Respectful and helpful especially to old people, Marina was doing her best to prevent his car from being scratched by the sign.

Everything happened so fast that I did not have time to utter a word of warning to her. When the car moved forward, instead of being scratched by the sign, it scraped skin of Marina's right hand. The senior citizen in the car did not even notice what happened and drove away. With a bleeding hand and tears in her eyes, Marina hurried to our car, where I used gauze from our emergency kit to take care of her wound. When the bleeding stopped, we went to the ER, where a hand fracture was ruled out. The relatively light trauma nevertheless caused significant pain in Marina's hand, a pain that began radiating to the right side of her chest. Her persistent cough made the chest pain unbearable. Seeing her suffering, I tried to persuade her to see her oncologist, but she stubbornly refused, telling me that she was coughing because of the chest pain. On the third day after the accident, Marina finally admitted that she needed to be checked by her oncologist. After the previous seven years free from manifestations of cancer, Dr. Arnold, who examined her, did not suspect anything serious and prescribed her codeine preparation. After four days of taking this medication, Marina's coughing did not , and at a follow-up visit, Dr. Arnold referred her to a pulmonologist.

Marina's seven years free of cancer so impressed the pulmonologist that when she let him know about the heartburn she'd begun to experience, not suspecting reoccurrence of cancer, he decided that her persistent cough was secondary to GERD, gastroesophageal reflux. He told her that acidic reflux, especially at nighttime, was aspirated into her lungs, where it irritated them and that produced her persistent cough. He prescribed a strong antacid medication, and "just in case," he ordered a chest X-ray and CT scan of her chest. At the end of the visit, Marina asked the pulmonologist to prescribe something other than codeine for her cough.

"Oh, that's not a problem," the pulmonologist reacted. "I am going to give you a miracle medication called Tussinex Perle, and I guarantee your stubborn cough will stop very soon." Tessalon Perle, or benzonatate, is a non-narcotic medicine that works by numbing the throat and lungs.

In a couple of days, Marina was done with the tests ordered by the pulmonologist. While she was waiting for the results, his prediction came true. Twenty-four hours of taking the prescribed medication passed, and her stubborn cough completely disappeared. Happy with the successful results, we thought the problem was over.

Alas, minutes of happiness do not last long.

Another thunder struck when our phone rang in the evening three days later. A nurse from oncology told Marina to come to discuss something important at Dr. Arnold's office the next day.

When we arrived, Marina was called to the examination room by a nurse right away. The moment the oncologist entered there, the nurse finished her exam. Greeting us quickly, and without preamble, looking intently into Marina's eyes, in a voice devoid of emotion, she told Marina that the CT scan had revealed she had metastases in her both lungs. Without doubt, these findings, she told, explained her persistent cough. The bad news we just heard in one moment shattered to pieces our irrational hopes that Marina's cancer had become dormant and inactive. Newly discovered metastases automatically transferred Marina's cancer to the terminal stage IV.

Marina, who never clung to life and for whom fear of death was alien, stayed true to herself, as it had happened many times before. She remained silent and serious, and her behavior did not betray any signs of panic or worry. Knowing her, I was sure that following her life motto "One day at a time," her mind was now preoccupied not with the future consequences of the menacing discovery but with the immediate effect of the news.

I wish that modern medicine could be as effective in the treatment of cancer as it had been with her stubborn cough. What a paradoxical creature is a human being. On the way home, Marina confessed to me that when she heard the terrible news about the reappearance of the cancer to her lungs, instead of being upset, she felt satisfied that at least she had gotten rid of her excruciating cough. Alas, with her cough gone she had won the battle, but she had lost the war with the cancer.

So, after the seven happy years, when the cancer was putatively under control, the day came for Marina to resume chemotherapy--the main weapon in the fight with the powerful inner enemy that never stopped its destructive work in her body.

What a tragic irony of human existence that the female breasts so beautifully, so harmoniously adorning the feminine body have the potential to become the Trojan horse that gradually destroys the life of that same body.

Cancer, Be Not Proud

The next evening, Marina got a call from Dr. Arnold, who told her that from added image studies she had established that Marina's metastases were present not only in her lungs but practically in all her long bones, and there was a vague suspicion that metastases were present in Marina's liver as well. Such a scary bouquet. Hence, after a seven-year break that had seemed to portend success, Marina's cancer was gradually winning new victories, spreading its destructive tentacles wherever it could reach. "Vacation" from disease was over, and now Marina needed to resume her battle for survival with renewed strength and dedication.

With time, in my mind, I figured out that the clinical course of a cancer is reminiscent of the movement of a heavily loaded freight train. Initially, the train moves slowly, as if it might stop anytime. However, when the train picks up a good speed, it seems that nothing can stop it from moving forward toward disaster.

When in 2005, Marina received her first combined chemotherapy, surgical, and radiation treatment, her cancer was still what one might call "unsophisticated," or "naïve." The cancerous cells had never been treated before, so they had a low degree of resistance to the treatments. Thanks to that, like many other patients in her position, Marina responded well to the first treatments. However, with each year and through many mutations, the cancerous cells became increasingly resistant. As a general rule, new strains of mutated cancerous cells are able to resist not only the body's natural immunity to aggressive intruders but also the action of different chemotherapeutic agents. When this happens, an oncologist, based on their experience and the generally accepted medical protocols of specific cancer treatments, will use a new chemotherapeutic agent, expecting a positive response. This said, there is never a guarantee that the new treatment will be the right method to destroy the newly mutated cancerous cells. In other words, it is impossible to know for sure which therapeutic drug is ideal in individual case. The oncologist does have an idea that this particular type of cancer and this particular illness dynamic could be affected by this or that group of available chemotherapy medications, but nobody knows for sure what the best choice is in each separate occurrence. Eventually, the malignant cells become more and more sophisticated in the production of new mutations that can withstand attempts to kill them with drugs, radiation, and other alternatives. When this happens, the body, in both the long and the short run, hardly has a chance for survival.

The confused genetics of cancer cells contradicts the universal biological tendency to contribute to the continuation of life. Quite the opposite—the cancer cells are themselves fatally damaging the host where they live. If normal cells do their utmost to help the survival of the organism as a whole, cancer cells "do not care" what is going to happen to the body. Figuratively speaking, the cancer cells care only about themselves and do not harmonize their needs with the entire body in which they dwell. Not affected by treatment, cancer cells tend to grow infinitely, eventually killing the body where they reside. The more these cells become destructive, the more they lose. Eventually, when these cells overwhelm the organism that constantly nourishes them, they commit biological suicide.

Cancer, be not proud.

Ron's Decision

It is intuitive to assume that people who have learned they have cancer will do all they can to fight it. However, a human being is a complicated creature, and as everyone might know, there are people who--for varied reasons--refuse the chance to prolong their life and instead choose to let nature run its course. These people, endowed with free will, represent a minority, but as long as their free will is accepted as given, they have the right to their individual decisions.

One of these persons was my old friend Ronald or Ron, a man in his early sixties, whom I regularly met in the neighborhood hardware store where he worked. Ron, a strong man of average height, was a valued expert at providing me with advice on how to take care of different do-it-yourself problems in my house. His glasses had thick lenses, and when it was necessary

AND AGAIN, THE STORM

for him to have a good look at an item under discussion, he would bring the glasses down from the top of his head to his nose, frown, and then, looking intently at the product, make his comment about it. Ron accompanied his words with a friendly smile that always lived in the corners of his mouth. Being a heavy smoker, he went through many cigarettes a day, smoking them with gusto. For many years in the past, he had been a carpet installer, which, as typically happens, left him with damaged knees and a slight lameness. We were good friends, so when I would find serious difficulties in fixing household items, he would leave the hardware store and come to my house to help me with solution of the complicated problem.

Ron lived not far from us, and early in the morning while driving with my wife on the way to prayer service, we frequently passed him on his way to work. Like a proud Roman warrior, he drove standing on the platform of his favorite Segway electric scooter. When he heard our loud greeting, he would turn his kind face toward us for a moment and would give us a wide smile.

One rainy day when Ron's scooter hit a poorly visible piece of metal on the sidewalk, he fell and landed on his chest, which resulted in a collapsed lung. Fortunately, the paramedics arrived in time, and with collapsed lung took him to a hospital where he was successfully operated on the same day.

Visiting the hardware store for a purchase, I saw my old friend, whom I knew for twenty years, standing in front of one of the aisles, sorting merchandise. The usual strong smell of tobacco surrounded him. We exchanged greetings, and I asked him what he was sorting on the shelf. Ron did not answer. Finally, when he turned to me, I saw on his face a bitter smile.

"What's the problem?" I asked, surprised.

"Well, the problem is that I developed a cough ten days ago," he responded. "The cough was so severe that my doctor sent me to Loyola University radiology. The result of the chest X-ray was so bad that they sent me to a cancer specialist—an oncologist, they called him. This cancer specialist ordered an MRI and body scan for me, and something else; I don't remember exactly what it was. To make a long story short, eventually the doctor tells me that I have a bad case of lung cancer and that I need to start treatment right away.

97

Well, after I thought it over, I decided to refuse from treatment. Period. *Que sera sera.*"

"But why don't you want to have treatment?" I asked him, shocked.

His answer followed after a long pause. "Because it will make me weak, tired, dependent, and disabled. I do not want that. That's not for me. I am going to run through whatever happens without treatment. The doctors didn't promise me anything good anyway."

For several minutes, I tried to persuade my good friend to change his mind, but his decision was unshakable.

In three weeks, when I saw Ron at the store again, the first thing I asked him was if he had changed his mind. When he gave a negative response, I tried to persuade him once again.

"Listen, Ron, I am sure you know that my wife, Marina, has had cancer for many years, and she fights it all the time," I said to him. "Treatment keeps her alive. Without it, she would have been dead a long time ago. Yes, she has side effects from treatment. Yes, it makes her tired, but she is alive, and she is happy to be among those who are alive. She does not complain, and she does not stop treatment. She does it not only for herself but also for the family, for me, for our children and grandchildren, and we are all are extremely happy that she is with us. Please, start treatment, Ron. It is not as difficult as you might think."

"Do not try to persuade me, my friend," Ron answered, pausing while lighting his next cigarette. "I've made up my mind, and it is final. Look at me. I am still strong, I am coughing much less, and I believe I have a chance to live without treatment for a while. Besides, I do not have anybody in the entire world, except my younger sister, who lives in Ohio. She has a husband and five children, and I am far from being important in her life. I am planning to work another couple of weeks in the store, and then I will finally fulfill my life plan. I will go to Hawaii, where I have my dream house, for which after thirty years, I recently finished to pay. It's on the North Shore of the Pacific Ocean, and believe me, the view there is breathtaking. I already have an airline ticket to go to Hawaii. Whatever time is left for me to live, I want to be there. With my bad case of cancer, I need to be in a hurry."

"Maybe we can agree on one point, Ron? At least, stop smoking."

"Come on, my friend, don't be ridiculous. In my state of health, smoking does not make any difference. I've smoked all my life, and I am not going to give it up now."

Marina and I spent the next couple of weeks taking care of our grandchildren in Milwaukee, and on the day after we returned, I went to the hardware store to see what was going on with my old friend. However, Ron was nowhere to be found.

When I saw Bob, the store owner, and asked him where Ron was, he replied that he had taken a couple of days off.

The next three weeks were quite busy for me, and when I was able to get back to the store, my friend was still not to be found.

"Where is Ron?" I asked Bob, who was busy working on the computer.

"Ron is dead," Bob answered simply, without taking his eyes off the computer screen.

"What do you mean dead?" I asked him again, shocked over tragic loss.

"He is dead, Vladimir. That's all I can tell you. Sorry, I am busy . . ."

"But that is terrible. He was such a great man," I said sadly.

"I know," Bob answered, turning his head in my direction. "He was a great help. There's no way I can replace him."

Bob was busy and visibly unwilling to discuss Ron's death. Not too many people like to talk about death, especially of a relative or a good friend.

Against my will, words escaped my mouth. "It's such a pity," I said. "Ron will never be able to enjoy his Hawaiian dream house."

"Man proposes, God disposes, Vladimir," followed Bob's short answer.

Such is life, I thought. Ron had been a tangible reality only a month ago, and now it looked as if he'd never worked in this store.

Marina and all the other people I met in the oncological unit were the direct opposite of Ron. Unlike him, they were determined to fight till the end. Though Marina now had numerous metastases in her body, she was far from among those who were ready to capitulate. For her, the spread of her cancer was a declaration of war, a signal for increased efforts to fight. She knew that she was not the first and would not be the last in this struggle.

Like a good chess player who does not give up even when left with minimal pieces, she was ready to continue her fight for survival. It was her credo that being temporarily in this world does not prevent us from loving and enjoying the incredible experience of being a participant in the daily celebration of life.

Fighting for Life

Like the majority of people in this world, until her last breath, Marina believed that our life is a gift of strength, provided to us by a force that some call God and some Destiny. Most of all, Marina believed that human life has a high hidden meaning. She lived one day at a time, and her appearance did not show a hint of anything that could be reminiscent of despair or shock. Following the words of Rudyard Kipling's poem "If—" Marina and those brave souls who fight cancer "can meet with Triumph and Disaster / And treat those two impostors just the same . . ."

"Hope" is the keyword describing the mobilizing force in our desire to live, in our desire to move forward. The determination of Marina and other victims to fight till the end best matches Winston Churchill's famous words "Never give in, never give in, never, never, never, never, in nothing, great or small, large or petty, never give in."

My wife continued to live with her chin up, never losing an iota of her dignity. Accompanying Marina to the numerous places in the oncological universe, I saw cancer patients of all ages, at different stages of their disease, and with personal tragedy. I saw women who did not show any signs of illness, and I saw women who bore the ravaging signs of their disease.

Women with signs of serious disease arrived with canes, with walkers, or in wheelchairs and were routinely coming in company with their caregivers. The universal and unforgettable feature that I saw daily was that they were calm and full of dignity. Among the numerous visitors to the oncological units we visited, I hardly remember seeing anybody in mental crisis. These countless people were nourished with indelible hope for an improvement from their present situation and hope for a better future. Obeying the powerful "love of life" code biologically embedded in the human soul, these people were ready to face challenging pain and discomforts sometimes associated with treatment in order to return to normalcy and once again enjoy life. Marina was one of these bright examples of the inexhaustible commitment to what she and others were doing.

As a rule, majority of oncologists see it as their moral responsibility to inspire hope in their patients. There are many ways to raise patients' spirits, one of which is to include a patient in one of many research studies that are always running in the teaching hospitals. Another way to comfort people in their health troubles is to remind the patient that science is constantly making progress in developing new, effective methods of treatment. For the most part, such reminders are effective in lifting the spirits of those who are going through this relentless disease.

Many patients who are enrolled in a research study in university centers are inspired by the notion that their suffering is not in vain and that it is an opportunity to help other people while helping themselves. This kind of encouragement helps patients feel more optimistic.

As a benefit, the patients who take part in the experimental study are enjoying added benefits such as more convenient times for appointments, priority in the scheduling of necessary tests, unlimited contact with the study nurse, and sometimes even financial reward. The patients in the trial had immediate access to the incoming experimental drug under study, which had already been proven to be effective in other stages of the research.

Marina satisfied necessary requirements and was accepted for participation in a research study supervised by a specially trained nurse, studying the effectiveness of a combination of two well-established chemotherapy medications—Xeloda, given orally, along with the experimental drug Ramucirumab, given intravenously. Weeks of receiving the medications alternated with weeks free from taking them. While on these medications, in addition to the common side effects of tiredness and low appetite, Marina experienced pain in her feet and hands, for which there were available effective lotions and ointments.

Surprisingly, though she had metastases in all her long bones, her bone marrow study was intact. On many occasions, it was proved that when she was not on chemotherapy treatment, she had normal levels of white and red blood cells as well as platelets in her peripheral blood. Thanks to this, she rarely needed added medication for the stimulation of blood formation by bone marrow, enabling her to receive uninterrupted treatment.

Being on chemotherapy does not mean the patient experiences continuous side effects. Most of the time, especially during days free from chemo, patients can return to their regular lives. Though the medication Xeloda was responsible for Marina's hair thinning, fortunately, it did not result in complete baldness. During the week free of treatment, her energy was quickly restored, allowing her to return to her normal routine.

Overall, the combination of Xeloda and Ramucirumab was highly effective. In two to three weeks, Marina stopped coughing and no longer needed the cough suppressor. Her MRI and bone scans clearly showed that the size of her lung metastases had stabilized and--oh, joy!-- had even shrunk to a significant degree.

Ever since Marina was diagnosed with cancer, she had done her best to control the hot flashes that continued to interfere with her life. In the incessant search for a possible solution to this problem, from time to time, she tried new psychotropic medications recommended by physicians. While they did not readily reduce her hot flashes, they did significantly affect her mood and appetite. To control the nagging and exhaustive hot flashes, all that remained were conservative measures, such as drinking ice water, wearing lesser layers of clothing, using handheld fans, and, in the winter, finding a place where it was cooler. During the cool season, it was on our porch, where she sat until the hot flashes subsided.

People with a normal psyche are not focused on their illness twenty-four hours a day, so when the current course of treatment was over, Marina and I did everything possible to enjoy our lives. Whether it was a coincidence or not, we did not know; however, on two occasions after airplane flights, she developed pneumonia, requiring her to be hospitalized. That was the reason why Marina did not want to travel by air any longer. But we continued to invite guests to our house and enjoyed visiting our relatives and friends locally. We went to see movies, plays, and operas, and when possible, we spent time with our children and grandchildren.

Young Children's Speech

When Marina was a teenager, she took part in her school puppet theater for many years, where she usually played the leading roles. A major indicator that she was in good spirits was her imitation of young children's speech or "baby-like talk." Many years ago, in Russia in 1964, together we read aloud Milne's book *Winnie-the-Pooh*, perfectly translated to Russian by the poet Boris Zakhoder. It became our favorite book, and ever since then, when we were in a good mood, Marina and I, spontaneously, without any preparation, impersonated the heroes of this remarkable book in our daily interrelation. Marina was Piglet, while I was Winnie-the-Pooh. Our close friends were so delighted by our innocent game that we became known as Piglet and Winnie-the-Pooh. This type of communication became a reliable barometer of Marina's mood. If she resorted to baby-like talk as if she were Piglet, it meant she was happy and joyful and that everything was going her way.

Grandchildren, as a Living Force

When Marina was with our grandchildren, even during periods of chemotherapy treatments, like the mythical phoenix, she continued miraculously to be transformed into the happiest person in the world. Never once would she miss an opportunity to be with our grandchildren. Taking care of them was the greatest joy for her. And naturally, her love for her grandchildren worked both ways.

To Live in the Present

Each course of chemo restored our hopes that the new medication would deceive the cancer and heal her. I was not as good as Marina at living one day at a time. If part of me lived in the raw reality, the other, irrational part of me, during life challenges, lived in constant expectation of a miracle. Perpetual hope never left me. What was the alternative? To be in a constant state of doom and gloom? No, that was neither for Marina nor for me. Since in my eyes my Marina was "a miracle incarnated," my vivid, surreal way of thinking made me believe she was an exception to the unshakable rules of nature. Each time when a new chemotherapy drug showed promising results, I forgot all that I heard from the oncologist about poor prognosis and persuaded myself that the new medication would help pull Marina from under the grinding wheels of the dreadful disease. As for Marina, she was a faithful follower of the famous Russian expression *"Бороться и искать, найти и не сдаваться,"* which could be translated as "Fight and seek, find and not give up."

As always, Marina took her illness philosophically and continued to avoid any discussions of what might happen to her in the future. On the issue of death, she spoke only when there was no other choice. Consciously and subconsciously, she was not afraid of death. There were no tragic monologues or scenes of despair. She lived as if everything that was happening was her transcended destiny. She said to me repeatedly that if she could not change the past and did not know what would happen in the future, all that was left for her was to learn how to be happy with the present concrete and tangible reality of the day. Once, in response to my skeptical remark about the current course of treatment, Marina smiled, and responded, "You might think that I'm stupid, but I don't really care much about the future. I am happy to be happy now, at this particular moment. That's the way I am."

From Xeloda to Eribulin

Our hopes that Xeloda would cure Marina were crushed in March 2013, when once again her scans showed an increase in size of her lungs' metastases. Even worse news was that the suspicious shadows in her liver were not suspicious anymore but showed themselves to be small tumors. On the top of it, her general health was worsening. Her energy level and appetite had decreased, and her spirits were dimmed. Based on these changes, Dr. Arnold stopped the Xeloda treatment and disenrolled her from the experimental study as well. Instead, she started Marina on another drug, Eribulin (generic name Halaven). Made from natural sea sponge, this medication was specifically used for the treatment of breast cancer, and it intended to stabilize cells. One cycle of treatment lasted twenty-one days and consisted of Eribulin intravenous infusion once a week for two weeks, then the patient was without it one week.

Failed Death Sentence

Initially, Marina's treatment with Eribulin resulted in clinical improvement, but that did not last long. Our hope for Eribulin's healing effects was dashed just four months after Marina started it. Instead of shrinking, her scans showed that her metastases were slowly increasing in size. In view of the lack of success, Dr. Arnold discontinued Eribulin and replaced it with another agent, Abraxane. Typically, Abraxane is used to treat advanced-stage breast cancer. It belongs to the class of taxane chemotherapy, a type of drug which by inhibiting the formation of the cellular structures helps move chromosomes during cell division, ideally eventually stopping the growth of the cancer. As with many other medications, Abraxane can cause the typical side effects of nausea, fatigue, and loss of appetite. It can also result in hair loss, damage to nerves, and changes in blood formation. Like Eribulin, Abraxane is given intravenously on days one, eight, and fifteen of each twenty-one-day cycle. Though Marina was able to tolerate it well during four months of June to September 2013, in the end it produced serious negative effects on her health. Alas, despite optimistic expectations, with time it was obvious that Marina could not tolerate this medication. She lacked energy and slept most of the day. One only had to take a quick look at her to understand that she was going through a difficult time. She did not complain—she hardly ever did—but during the daytime, when she was awake, tired, and lacking energy, she sat motionless on her favorite armchair in her room for hours and stared straight ahead with her eyes widely open. Other side effects of Abraxane included nausea, lack of appetite, and aversion to food. With every new day, Marina's condition worsened. A medication for nausea stopped helping her. To get her to eat, I offered her all kinds of edibles, almost all of which she would refuse. Nutrition drinks she refused to drink, mostly because they were "too sweet" for her. When, following much persuasion, she finally agreed to drink one, shortly she would develop severe nausea and heartburn. In a short period of time, she had lost several pounds and became very thin. The foods she did tolerate were freshly-made-from-scratch chicken soup, milkshakes, and especially Haagen-Dazs dark-chocolate ice cream bars, all of which were the only food she ate for the entire day. When it came time for the third injection of Abraxane, her energy level was so low that when she contacted the unit's nurse and described her condition, the nurse told her to see Dr. Arnold the next day.

When we got to the parking lot, Marina was so weak that I had to take her in a wheelchair. The main hospital parking lot was always busy during working hours. Significant number of people who came to the university for medical appointments were permanently or temporarily disabled. Some of the patients had their own wheelchairs, but patients like Marina, who had just recently lost their strength, needed wheelchairs only when they came for an appointment. Fortunately, on each floor of the parking structure, especially in the area next to the elevators, wheelchairs could almost always be found, left after a patient was delivered to the parking lot either by their caregivers or by hospital transporters. Because Marina was not able to walk more than a few steps during her difficult periods, the availability of a wheelchair was a precious help.

On that day, she waited in the car while I found a wheelchair and returned with it to our car. It was heartbreaking to see how my wife, who only recently had been so active and full of energy, was slow and had difficulty getting out of the car and then taking seat in the wheelchair.

When the receptionist in the waiting room noticed Marina's condition, she at once called a nurse to take her to the exam room. In the exam room, after helping her onto the exam table, this nurse asked a couple of questions, took Marina's vital signs, and exited the room, forgetting or not paying attention that Marina was left sitting in the upright position without back support--a frequent situation in medical offices. To help her I rose the back leaf of the exam table.

We were looking forward to the arrival of Dr. Arnold. Only she, an oncologist with great experience, could find the right solution to the present worrying situation. As it was mentioned, choosing a chemotherapy drug for treatment by the doctor is a matter of trial and error. Since Abraxane turned out to disagree with Marina, we hoped the doctor's choice for the next medication would be more appropriate.

Soon, we heard light knocking, and in the exam room entered a medical student. While Marina answered his questions, he made notes in his notebook. When Marina repeated how bad she felt lately, he nodded in understanding and left us, saying he would come back soon with Dr. Arnold. Indeed, shortly Dr. Arnold and he entered the exam room. By that time, we had known Dr. Arnold for one and a half years and were on good terms with her. However, that day she greeted us in an emphatically detached and formal manner. Sitting on a chair, not taking her eyes off Marina, she was all attention to what Marina was saying. Looking at her, one might think that she intended to say something important. After Marina finished, without saying a word, still much more reserved than during previous visits, she performed Marina's physical examination. Eventually she took a seat and resumed the conversation.

"My medical student already conveyed to me your complaints, Mrs. Tsesis, and indeed, you do not look good today," she said, her face finally expressing formal concern and thoughtfulness. "Obviously, Abraxane does not agree with you but as I remember you did not do well with Eribulin as well. So, it is not only the chemotherapy drugs that affect you. After all, you should not forget about your main issue, about the numerous metastases that are responsible for your condition. How could you summarize your complaints, please?"

"I feel extremely tired, Dr. Arnold," Marina responded in a weak monotone. "I am doing my best to pull myself out of my misery, but I can't. I thought maybe you can discontinue Abraxane and exchange it for something else. I am sorry I feel so bad."

"You should not be sorry that you do not feel good, Mrs. Tsesis. Unfortunately, I observe similar situations with other patients day in and day out. Well, as your doctor, I do not have any choice but to tell you the naked truth. It appears that despite the best intention, we have reached an impasse. Since we tried all kinds of chemo drugs and there was not a good response, it appears to me that we have run out of options. I think it is time for us to stop your treatment and let the nature run its course. You do not respond to treatment anyway."

The oncologist's words produced a loud explosion in my mind, but I remained silent.

"Dr. Arnold, I responded to chemotherapy well in the past," Marina objected quiet but firm. "I think you should start me on something else than Abraxane?"

"At this stage, I cannot think of anything else that might help you," the doctor answered categorically, "and I have no other choice but to say that it will be best if we stop giving you any treatment whatsoever."

"But without treatment, I will be lost. What will help me without treatment?" Marina asked, not losing her presence of mind and looking intently at Dr. Arnold with tired and narrowed eyes.

"The same thing that has happened with thousands of my patients before," Dr. Arnold answered in a cold, unapologetic, and detached tone. "My nurse practitioner and social worker will talk to you about placing you in hospice care. I am sure this is the best choice in the situation you are now, Mrs. Tsesis. I guarantee they will take excellent care of you there. With hospice care, you will neither suffer nor have any pain."

Inside of me, everything was boiling. Unlike many other physicians, Dr. Arnold usually welcomed the participation of a caregiver in a conversation, but today she deliberately ignored me. As a doctor, I explained for myself the lack of desire to listen to a caregiver for three reasons. The first is physician's overzealousness in following the rules of privacy. The second is that the doctor considers the caregiver's interference as an unnecessary distraction that prolongs the appointment, and the third reason is that the doctor is justifiably or unjustifiably annoyed by somebody who interferes in a conversation without permission or invitation. In the past, Dr. Arnold had not had any of those attitudes and never stopped me from asking questions and making short remarks.

Up to the moment when Dr. Arnold mentioned hospice care second time, I had sat silently, trying not to interfere with the conversation between her and my wife. However, what the oncologist had just reiterated in such an impassive tone of voice was too hard to take. Not able to be silent anymore, I leaped to my feet and said in a resolute tone, "Absolutely not! Absolutely not! We are far from giving up, Dr. Arnold, and to capitulate is not in our agenda. The fight for my wife's life is far from being over. Remember what I say: hospice is not for her! She will continue to receive treatment."

My words did not produce any visible changes on the doctor's face. All who were present in the examination room were expecting what she was going to say.

"In that case, we will have a break in treatment for two months so your wife can regain her strength," Dr. Arnold said after a short pause. She said it in a business-like manner as if absolutely nothing dramatic had taken place a moment ago, as if only a minute ago issue of life and death was not on the agenda, when she recommended to say goodbye to life to her patient. "After two months, I will start you, Mrs. Tsesis, on a different medication."

The oncologist's words revived Marina, whose fate could be decided at that very moment. "How can I be without treatment for two months?" she asked in a low voice. "I am afraid that my untreated cancer will grow enough to destroy me in two months."

"You should not worry. The problem with a cancerous tumor of your type is not that it grows quickly, but that it does not respond well to treatment. I expect to see you again in two months."

Returning home, we hardly exchanged a word. Marina shared my recent ironclad intention to not surrender to Dr. Arnold's suggestion. We both thought that a doctor was supposed to be a captain of a sinking ship, encouraging the crew not to surrender to the mercy of the victor. In any case for Marina and me, the battle with cancer was far from being lost. Our optimistic assessment of the situation was not a blind, emotional conclusion but was based on the objective facts. Before the treatment with Abraxane, Marina had been strong enough to be active enough to lead a normal life; for example, performing practically all the household chores. She continued to like her autonomy, and if I tried to help her with something that appeared to be too difficult for her to deal with, she resolutely refused my help, trying to prove for herself--not for me, but for herself--that she was still is an independent woman who did not need help. Also, we did not forget how strong and full of energy she became when she had an opportunity to spend time with our grandchildren, which invariably produced a powerful revitalizing effect on her. Unlike our oncologist's death sentence, Marina and I agreed that the current problem was not with Marina's body, but specifically with Abraxane, which was not compatible with her body.

In the evening, we spoke with our children. Alexandra, a general surgeon, got in touch with two friends from her residency who were now practicing oncologists. The consensus was that indeed it was too early to give up and that a new medication would hopefully be effective and pull Marina from her current condition. Knowledge is power, and after all the discussions, it was concluded that there was still a good chance for effectively controlling Marina's progressing disease.

During the pause in her treatment, although the cancer slowly but surely continued its dastardly action, with every day, Marina became more active. After a week without chemotherapy, her general health had improved, proving what we knew—the main culprit for her sharp deterioration was not her malignancy but Abraxane's side effects. Despite all the recent turmoil, we lived as though nothing special was happening and did not think overly about the present state of Marina's health. We did not do it intentionally. Life is life, and a normal human being cannot think about his or her health all the time. The only change was that we stopped traveling, which before Marina's illness, we had enjoyed doing often. The main reason for this change was that Marina lost her taste for travel; she steadfastly refused to go anywhere on a long trip. The two earlier airplane journeys, which had ended with pneumonia, were enough for her to not want to travel. In any case, it was not a problem; we had plenty to do with our lives without taking trips. Marina's main pastime remained her lifelong love of reading. She read quickly and went through many books; she knew well Russian, American, and Israeli literature. To her credit, she had successfully passed on her love of reading to our grandchildren. To make sure it stuck, she periodically bought children's books that our grandchildren read and then she discussed these books with them by phone or in person.

CHAPTER 5

Escape from Hospice

Break in Treatment

Significant health problems that might occur in our life require independent thinking and critical attitude to the advice of even a famous doctor. There is nothing more precious than the human life. God forbid if we had followed the directions of our so reputable, so well-known, so respected, and so experienced Dr. Arnold, which she gave Marina at that fateful visit. Our oncologist's proposal would steal from Marina the whole five years of her life. If we followed what Dr. Arnold so categorically suggested, Marina would definitely have been dead in the span of the next six months, at the age of seventy. Instead, she lived a constructive and busy life for another five long years that could not be stolen from her!

In the following days, seeing how Marina became stronger every day after Abraxane was stopped, our impression was confirmed that Dr. Arnold had made a serious medical mistake, in effect sentencing her patient to an untimely death.

It might be difficult to understand, but Marina did not change her doctor, continuing to remain Dr. Arnold's patient. The main reason was that we simply did not know any alternative. What if a new physician's bedside manner turned out to be the same or even worse than the present one? In the event that our doctor had ever undergone the investigation by an authority to explain her decision to cruelly and wrongly urge her patient to enter hospice, the doctor, without batting an eye, would justify her decision using two magical phrases that served as a universal doctors' alibi: "It was my clinical decision" and "I based it on my previous clinical experience." It was fortunate that Marina had doctors and friends within our family who could give her a good advice. But what could happen with the countless seriously ill people who are not educated well and who do not have an opportunity for a second opinion? Tears of many victims are invisible to the world.

Treatment Resumes

Two and a half months went by fast, and Marina, with her strength restored, returned to Dr. Arnold. Our hope for Marina's long survival had not deserted us after the recent bad experience. My basic reasoning had not changed. If her condition had improved so nicely for these weeks, then maybe her cancer would finally begin "to hibernate" and leave my dear wife alone. However, when I faced the real world, I realized that I'd ignored the presence of a large number of cancer metastases in her body. In any case, in the conflict between rational and irrational thinking, the sacred word "hope" continued to light up brightly my mind. As for Marina, she did not give up her usual strategy, taking things one day at a time and staying away from thoughts of the future. As always, her thoughts were concentrated mostly on the welfare of the present moment. There was an even more important reason why she would never think about surrendering to the disease: she fought in the name of a family for which she felt a sacred responsibility.

As before, Marina received her treatment at the oncological treatment center where Dr. Arnold practiced. The established routine of our visits was simple. In the morning, we would arrive at the parking structure. Then Marina, walking on her own, or, depending on her condition, sometimes being pushed by me in a wheelchair, would enter the treatment center. Usually, we arrived for the appointment forty minutes before the scheduled time and at once went straight to the cafeteria, where we ordered our favorite sesame seed bagels and cream cheese, tea for Marina, and coffee for me. These visits were for us very important from a psychological point of view. Being in the cafeteria and enjoying breakfast always helped us to temporarily forget about our worries and anxieties. It was extremely pleasant for both of us, best friends, to sit across from each other, to look each other in the eyes, and immensely enjoy delicious food but mostly each other's company. Though we were within the walls of the hospital, during these divine moments, we temporarily forgot about illness and unpleasant news.

Experiencing the undoubtful psychological healing effects of bagels and cream cheese we would go up to the treatment center, register there, and take seats in the large waiting area. Marina would be called in for the lab tests, the result of which figured out whether she could receive chemo that day. Usually, Marina's tests, which gauged the general health of a patient, were normal, other than rare cases when her red blood cell count was too low. When she was done with her blood tests, she would come back to the waiting room, and soon she would be called in for her treatment appointment. I was always more than welcome to go with her. A nurse would let Marina know the results of today's blood test and if the result was good, she would receive the scheduled treatment. It happened rarely that the lab result was abnormal, but when it was, Marina's attending physician or nurse practitioner without delay provided her with medication to take care of the current problem. In case of a serious problem, she was told when to return for treatment and was given recommendations what to do in the meantime.

The treatment center unit always kept to a strict schedule, and patients never had to wait long to receive their chemotherapy treatments. The waiting room was always occupied by patients and their caregivers. The patients were waiting to be called by nurses to be examined by their doctors for blood tests and for other procedures. Most of the women and rarely men who might have oncological diseases could not be easily distinguished in the crowd. However, having had ample opportunity to observe closer and critically those around me in the waiting room, with time, I could see that as a rule people on the treatment lacked energy. There were always women who were bald headed and others who wore headcovers of different types. There were some patients in wheelchairs and some who used walkers. The most dramatic to see were the young women with oncological problem, who were just at the beginning of their lives. At the sight of them, Marina never failed to comment again and again on how lucky she was for getting the disease at a later age. I do not remember ever seeing young children. Their parents would not bring them to the place where the forces of life were confronted by opposite powers.

Patients disabled by their disease received their treatment in the separate, well-equipped rooms with wide windows looking out at the corridor. To avoid the toxic effect of chemo on their own health, the nurses wore special gloves and extra gowns. Although adequate privacy was offered via a set of curtains that could surround each separate patient, the majority of patients preferred not to separate themselves from the others. With the inherent solidarity of people who are in trouble, patients at the treatment center wanted to share their health-related histories with their comrades in misfortune. Like strangers who met on a train and would never see each other ever again, they eagerly conversed with their companions, sharing not only their stories but also their intimate concerns and worries. It was remarkable that I never met anybody who was dramatic during such interactions. Everyone spoke business like, knowing well that those who listened understood them far more than anybody who did not go through the ordeal they went through.

Almost all the patients in the waiting room were accompanied by relatives or friends, which once again convinced me that people are fundamentally good. The expressions on the faces of the people sitting in the waiting room showed a strong, unquenchable hope for a favorable outcome. This hope was reinforced by the promises of the current treatment and by knowledge that they were not alone in the time of trouble. It goes without saying that being together with someone during major life challenges is better than being alone. What, in principle, is the difference between the destiny of a healthy person and a person who has a terminal disease? While it is only the factor of time, the majority healthy people have a feeling that their life will never end. Of the many cancer patients with whom I spoke at the cancer facilities over many years, I can hardly remember anybody who did not believe that treatment would prolong their life. Time after time, I was impressed with cancer patients' general resilience and their ability to cope and recover quickly after unfavorable news. Time was a factor that was beyond discussions. Again and again, I observed that hope is mankind's mighty saving force. American psychologist George Weinberg put it well: "Hope never abandons you, you abandon it."

Two months later, at the first visit after Abraxane was discontinued, Dr. Arnold attentively listened to Marina, who told her what our professional friends' recommendation for the present situation were. After listening to Marina, Dr. Arnold told her that, in principle, she agreed with our professional friends and that she planned to order a new cycle of chemotherapy treatment for Marina with the medication Faslodex.

Faslodex is a strong antiestrogen medication that inhibits the growth of cancer cells. Its main use is limited to postmenopausal women with advanced hormone-related breast cancer that has spread to other parts of the body. By blocking the actions of the estrogen, Faslodex deprives the tumor cells of the major stimulant of their growth. The side effects of Faslodex are similar to many other anticancer medications, and the main question before us was will Faslodex be effective for Marina, will she tolerate it and for how long?

Faslodex is given as two injections, one into the muscle of each buttock. Each injection must be given slowly and can take up to two minutes to complete. Depending on the chosen schedule of treatment, it can be given once, twice, or three times per month.

Despite many side effects of Faslodex, overall, Marina ended up tolerating it well. Her side effects included signs of nerve damage such as numbness, tingling, and weakness in her back and legs. Also, sometimes she got tired and had a poor appetite.

At any time of the day, Marina's hot flashes continued to torment her, stubbornly persisting in waking her up several times during the night. Night sweats forced her to change her nightgown every time she woke up. Eventually, it was her idea for us to sleep in separate rooms. We both appreciated how lucky we were to have enough space in our home to live in comfortable conditions.

As it was before, no medication was helping Marina with her hot flashes. I knew that a new episode was coming when I saw perspiration appearing on her forehead and her visible skin becoming red and blotchy. Over time, Marina developed her own strategy dealing with her unpleasant condition. During the winter when she felt a new bout of hot flashes approaching, she left the room and retired to the porch, where the temperature was cooler. She would sit on a little sofa until her symptoms went away, which could last between five and fifteen minutes. During the warm season, her best friend was a floor fan.

Doctor and Medical Ethics

In addition to Dr. Arnold's misguided hospice advice, there was another occurrence when our renowned oncologist was not perfect. This happened during one of Marina's appointments in May 2015. By this time, we had known Dr. Arnold for over three years.

During this visit, when after one and a half years of treatment Faslodex had returned Marina to good health, Dr. Arnold, being not too busy, was unusually informal. Under a continuous spell of hope and expecting encouraging news, Marina and I were relaxed and felt secure with her medical management. As we expected, at the end of Marina's short physical examination, Dr. Arnold told her that she was doing well. Marina thanked her for the good news and then asked her about her family's well-being. A short conversation about the doctor's and our families ensued, after which the topic of conversation changed to general life issues. During one of the pauses in the talk, Marina mentioned that she felt sorry when she had seen a young woman in obvious distress in the waiting room.

Judging by Dr. Arnold's facial expression, it seemed she knew well who Marina was talking about. She nodded her head knowingly, letting us know that she was in solidarity with Marina on the plight of the poor young lady. "I also feel sorry for this young lady," she said. "It's not a news for anybody that we are all mortal. We doctors are not gods. We do our best to help people, but we cannot be always successful. Sooner or later, one of our patients becomes eligible for hospice care, if not worse. When this tragic moment comes, we can only tell ourselves that we must let nature take its course. I must confess that sometimes I think those people who support euthanasia might be right, you know. When, by the nature of my profession, I see how futile our heroic measures are to save the lives of some of my patients, I confess that inside I want to yell 'That's enough!' Of course, I am not allowed to say that out loud."

What she'd just said about euthanasia was a second blow to Marina, after the one that had happened earlier when Dr. Arnold was ready to write her off from among the living with her indisputable suggestion that Marina become a hospice patient.

"I do not have a contact with God to know when I want to say goodbye to my life," Marina interrupted the doctor sharply, pale and visibly shaken. "It is not because I am afraid to die, but euthanasia is not for me."

It was the first and the last time when Marina expressed to the doctor her opinion about an important issue. After a short pause that ensued in the room, Marina continued, "I do not know about you, Dr. Arnold, but I live each day as if life just started. I might be living in illusion, but it is an illusion of my own choice. Presently I am alive, and when death comes, I am not going to fight it. But I do not want anybody, including you or anybody else, to discuss when it's my time to die. It is not you who gave me my life and it's not up to you to decide whether I should continue to live on or not. Before the eternity, we are all equal. Now please stop this conversation about death. It is neither time nor place for such a conversation."

The doctor can not only help patients but also harm them. That's why the main principle of the Hippocratic Oath is "First do not harm." The ideas that Dr. Arnold was sharing with us belonged to an academic medical ethics discourse. To discuss them with a patient in Marina's condition was unforgivably cruel and contradicted the purpose and essence of the practice of medicine. The essence of the physician's profession is the responsibility to treat people, not to get rid of people who are disabled or who are not productive. I wonder how Dr. Arnold would feel if she herself were in the place of the patient for whom she just gave a hint that it comes a time when patients should give up their struggle for life and be a subject for preparation for euthanasia. "Just forget what I said," Dr. Arnold responded when Marina stopped not showing signs of embarrassment and regret. "I agree that I was expressing something I should keep to myself."

Even after this episode, we did not leave our doctor. It was not only because of the mentioned earlier reason, but that for us, there was no way to know if another doctor might be better. Maybe there was a better physician for Marina, but how could we know that the new physician would not blindside us with another shocking suggestion? After all, among other oncologists on the university hospital staff, Dr. Arnold was considered to be outstanding. Besides, Dr. Arnold knew Marina's complicated health history well, and it would be not wise "to change horses in midstream." As for Dr. Arnold's opinions about life and death, the last word about such issues would be Marina's and mine anyway. On the other hand, we did not doubt that Dr. Arnold would try to do everything proper to provide Marina with the appropriate medical care. We were not the first who chose a doctor not for their religious, social, or philosophical views, but for their skill in providing the best possible treatment. The only outcome of the euthanasia conversation was that our attitude toward our physician became less cordial than it had been before.

Unanswered Question

Marina's improvement when she was treated with Faslodex was so impressive that I, in my inextinguishable, surreal dream of a remission, on a couple of occasions asked Dr. Arnold if Marina really needed to have her MRI and bone scan every three months. Most possibly assuming that being a physician I should know the reason for these tests, she responded to my questions with silence. Obviously, she could not understand that a pediatrician might not know the details of the clinical course of a disease where she was a specialist. I could not have a clear understanding of the natural course of cancer. If she had not assumed that I have knowledge in the field of medicine that was unfamiliar to me and took just a moment of her time to explain what was going on, I would not have asked her such, as I understand later, "a naïve question." In any case, as long before, my unquenchable hope had made me forget about the insidious nature of Marina's illness. As for Marina, she never betrayed her motto to live for today. These months were so incredibly relaxed and happy that after a pause that had lasted years, as from nowhere we resumed our Piglet and Winnie-the-Pooh baby-like talk. Full of happiness, I played along with our game during this fortunate moment in our lives.

Genetics Did Not Disappoint

During this respite from the challenges of Marina's illness, one day she read in a health magazine an article about the genetics of breast cancer, and that excited her.

"We have to do something," she told me in an alarmed tone that day. "Listen to me, Vovka. Before I read this article, I knew nothing about important details of the genetic predisposition for breast cancer. Reading this article, I realize suddenly that we should make sure our granddaughter Ruthie, God forbid, did not inherit that predisposition from me. I must find out as soon as possible if I have the BRCA gene, which might affect our Ruthie if she inherited it. I have already scheduled an appointment with the genetic specialist at the university hospital to check if I have the BRCA gene."

The next week, we went to the laboratory. Marina's blood was taken for a genetic study, and a couple of weeks later, we met with two genetic specialists to hear the results of the test. Marina was quite nervous; she could not hide her apprehension that she could possibly have passed the unfavorable gene to her beloved granddaughter. Her beautiful eyes were wide open, and her hands were slightly shaking, betraying her inner tension.

After a light conversation, one of the geneticists opened a folder and began to read aloud a long report. Neither Marina nor I understood much of what we heard, and with impatience we waited for the conclusion of the report.

Finally, the moment came. The female geneticist who had read the report closed the folder and looked at my wife. "Do not worry, Mrs. Tsesis," she said, changing her previously official tone to cordial. "Calm down; you do not have the BRCA gene, and therefore, there is no way you could have transmitted it to your granddaughter."

A sigh of relief burst from the chest of my wife. Her face was beaming with joy. "See, there is God, Vovka," she told me excitedly. "So, thank God, I will not be the source of troubles for my Ruthie in the future!"

Meanwhile, thanks to the Faslodex medication, Marina continued to be in good physical and spiritual shape. The sky above us was strewn with diamonds. Forgetting the constant warnings of our medical caregivers about how insidious and treacherous Marina's condition could be and that without treatment her life might end in six months, like many people in our place, we tried to live as if the cancer was not knocking at our door. We were protected from obsessive worries about Marina's health by the overwhelming sense of hope naturally found in the heart of people.

Fighting Lymphedema

At the beginning of 2014, the time she was still on Faslodex medicine, Marina's condition was so good that we went for a trip, first to Mexico and then to Florida. Together with our good friends who went with us, we had a wonderful time. Marina never liked hearing words of sympathy about her health. Deciding that she should have nice appearance, she tried to groom herself in the best possible way. Her hair at that time was in reasonable condition, and she gave it the best possible care. She never missed a visit to the beauty salon, where she had a manicure and pedicure regularly. Now she was buying clothes from more expensive stores and catalogues. I was glad to support her in this endeavor and actively took part in discussions about new acquisitions. Was it an optical illusion or a benign prejudice? But it appeared to me that among the other women whom I knew, she was always the best dressed one.

At this relaxed period of our life, in popular magazine dedicated to the education of patients with neoplasms, Marina read an article about lymphedema. Lymph, a derivate of blood plasma, is the tissue fluid found in the spaces around cells that impregnate or wash mainly the muscle system. Removal of lymph nodes from the armpit results in the impairment of the fluid's circulation and leads to the swelling of the affected flesh. As it could be expected, the removal of Marina's lymph nodes during her mastectomy in 2005 resulted in lymphedema of the corresponding arm. To Marina's eyes, the relatively slight swelling of her arm appeared to be much larger than it really was. On the internet she read that with time the arm with compromised lymphatic circulation might swell to such a degree that the lymphatic fluid could perspire from the inside all the way out to the skin's surface, and this sweat-like substance would make the skin disgustingly smelly and sticky. I was sure that the degree of Marina's lymphedema was light-years away from what she was imagining, but I did not want to contradict her. In order to learn how to manage such a condition, I was happy to go with her to a surgeon. Even though, like me, the surgeon who examined Marina was not concerned about the degree of her arm's swelling and did not think it demanded special medical attention, Marina became obsessed with the long-term consequences of her lymphedema. I, who tried to be her faithful knight, did not want to disagree with her because, on the positive side, worry about her lymphedema distracted her from much more disturbing thoughts. It was much better for her to worry about such a minor problem rather than focusing on the main trouble with her health.

We set out to manage Marina's left arm's swelling by using common sense. Twice a day, I "milked" her arm by first clasping my fingers at the wrist level of her lower arm, and then, applying pressure by tightly squeezing my clasped fingers, I moved them upward, trying to move the lymph fluid that had accumulated in the arm toward the armpit. We expected that this fluid would then flow into the general lymphatic circulation. Since all of Marina's lymph nodes had been removed, we expected the lymph fluid would drain through the arm's microscopic collateral capillaries. After each procedure, we would think we saw an improvement, but after several months, the swelling did not decrease. So to deal with the problem, Marina made an appointment with a physiotherapist at the local hospital.

I might have been mistaken, but judging by my earlier experience, I concluded that while without doubt physiotherapy is an effective tool for the treatment of acute medical problems, it is much less effective in the treatment of many chronic conditions. At least in Marina's case, my judgment proved correct. The physiotherapist, a nice woman, performed the same milking procedure as I had done at home, with, as I expected, the same zero effect.

After another two months of unsuccessful attempts to reduce the lymphedema in her arm, Marina politely asked her current physiotherapist if it was possible to refer her to a physiotherapist who had experience with her medical condition. The physiotherapist agreed, and the same day Marina was examined and treated by another physiotherapist who had an experience in different approaches to the treatment of lymphedema. For the next month, twice a week, Marina visited the new physiotherapist, who tried different methods of intervention. None of them worked until finally Marina learned from her about the availability of an effective method of treatment. It turned out that the proper drainage of lymph fluid could be efficiently carried out with a special device called a sequential circulator, a unit with an electric compressor, which provides the same milking effect as the manual method, but it works much more effectively. A sequential circulator machine that we obtained allowed Marina do the treatment at home. As an exemplary patient, Marina did not miss a single scheduled procedure. After three months of treatment at home, she achieved good results, and after that she never needed to use the device again; her lymphedema disappeared. Since then, we asked specialists why she had not needed more treatments, but nobody could give us a satisfactory explanation. Most probably, some structural changes took place in the connective tissue of the affected arm, which took care of her problem.

Grandmother and Grandchildren

Marina loved her grandchildren deeply and unconditionally. By 2013, our son and his family had moved from Milwaukee to the Chicago area. When Ruthie was ten, Ariel was eight, and Marina was seventy, Marina began to volunteer at their Solomon Schechter School so she would have an opportunity to see them twice a week. The school was located quite far from our house, but Marina had enough energy to not only drive there but also spend four hours working in the school library. Her job was to put books on shelves according to the established library system and to answer children's questions about books. She liked her work in the library, but the main attraction for her was that, especially during the long lunch recess, she had a chance to meet with her grandchildren. Not far from the school was a coffee shop where Marina used to stop on the way to school and buy the children's favorite sesame seed bagels with cream cheese. Using a hot pack and a blanket, she kept the bagels warm, and when one or both grandchildren would come to the library during lunch, she had for them warm lunch and the treats. The children loved their grandmother's lunches. The food was not too different from the school meals, but it was precious because their grandmother prepared it especially for them. Sometimes Ruthie or Ariel brought their friends to the library, and everyone had a great time. The children loved spending time together, and Marina got great pleasure and inspiration being in the company of her beloved grandchildren and their friends. With no doubt, the pleasure of being together was mutual.

When the grandchildren could not come to the library, Marina found them in one of their classrooms and made sure they received the treats. Whenever there was an opportunity, they all went to the cafeteria or to a secluded place at the school. Marina believed that rather than giving gifts to her grandchildren, it was much more important to spend time with them. Ruthie and Ariel's parents spent plenty of time with children, but when they were busy, Marina and I would often take the children to museums, the theater, or different shows. One of our favorite shows that we tried to never miss was Tchaikovsky's ballet *The Nutcracker*, outstandingly performed by the Joffrey Ballet in Chicago, every Christmas. Long before the show premiered, Marina would order tickets for the entire family in the theater's best box seats. This cherished tradition only could stop her death.

Oncologist Dr. Miller

In 2014, while Marina's cancer continued to be successfully controlled by Faslodex, Dr. Arnold left Chicago to take the position of director at a cancer unit in one of the northern states. Believing that the quality of treatment largely depended on who was the attending physician, Marina and I began a search for another doctor who was not only experienced in treatment but also personable and attentive. In the search we followed the unwritten golden rule of American medicine that the best way to find a good doctor was by word of mouth. With the help of our friends and acquaintances, we looked for a physician who would be trustworthy and excellent at coming to tactical and strategic decisions.

Soon, our friends strongly recommended to us Dr. Debra Miller. She was on the staff of another university hospital than Dr. Arnold. This oncological center was not as luxurious as the earlier center, but it was more than good enough for us.

Our first visit to Dr. Miller made a good impression on Marina. The main conclusion we gleaned from the visit was that, among other positive characteristics, this doctor had the valuable quality of keeping her patients' hope on the high level. It was obvious for us that she strongly believed that keeping hope in her patients had a powerful therapeutic effect and that it helped them to overcome the daily challenges of life.

Marina and I were happy with our new doctor. From the earlier experience, we knew that it was a great art to deliver bad news while not shaking a patient's sense of hope and to reassure them that they received the best possible treatment for their condition. Later, Marina and I had multiple opportunities to see our new doctor's ability to prove to her patients that in many challenging situations, "the glass was still half full."

New Treatment (or Procedure) Center

Our new oncologist's treatment center was found on the same floor as the doctors' offices, but it was designed differently from the one we'd gone to with our previous physician. In the earlier medical practice, the treatment center had consisted of a general area and several separate rooms, but this center consisted of one huge hall that occupied half of the entire floor, with wide windows facing east, south, and west. The practitioners in Dr. Debra Miller's group took care of not only breast cancer patients but patients with all kinds of oncological problems. On one side of the treatment center was a large station for nurses and auxiliary staff. Volunteers helped the staff to provide the best possible care to the numerous patients. In the center of the hall was an area where patients and those who accompanied them could help themselves to coffee, tea, and crackers. In the front of the hall stood a couple of large tables. One of them held informational materials, and the other held high-quality used books that patients could take home if they wanted.

Each patient received treatment while sitting on a comfortable La-Z-Boy recliner, and the accompanying caregivers were given standard armchairs. In the treatment center, everybody was equal; it functioned on a first-come-first-served basis, and anyone could claim any available seat. Just as in the earlier treatment center, the staff of the new center took excellent care of the patients, and privacy was provided in the usual way, with a circular curtain that came down from the ceiling. As it was before, patients going through their individual tragedy hardly ever hid behind the curtain, and at the first opportunity, they willingly communicated with their companions in misfortune.

Those patients who knew their procedure would take a long time brought food with them, which they washed down with the free drinks. It was touching to see the caregivers, especially the spouses, bustle around, offering their charges all kinds of treats.

The words of praise could be said of the staff in the office area where the physicians saw their patients. As I saw many times, those medics who worked in oncological services were unfailingly respectful, cordial, and professional. I think that such a positive attitude is the result of the nature of their work, but I also learned that when hiring for oncological services, the hospitals recruited nurses with higher qualifications. Working with patients, some of whom might be facing a tragic outcome in the foreseeable future, the entire staff was inspired by the knowledge that their work had great value and meaning.

None of Us Is Perfect

From the beginning, Marina and I concluded that Dr. Miller had been a good choice as Marina's oncologist. However, nobody is perfect; for example, we could not understand Dr. Miller's way of reporting to patients the results of important diagnostic procedures such as MRIs, CTs, and bone scans. When Marina was under Dr. Arnold's care, the doctor or her nurse practitioner always called us at home at the end of the same day the tests were performed, letting us know the results.

Unfortunately, Dr. Miller's routine was to let her patients know the results of CTs, MRIs, and bone scans not on the same day but when patients came to her office for their next visit in one, two, or three days. The doctor, whom we firmly believed to be perceptive and compassionate, for some reason, refused to understand how worried her patients might be anticipating the results of their body imaging. It was strange that the sensitive doctor underestimated how impatiently and anxiously her patients awaited the results of tests that would inform them about changes in the status of their oncological disorder. If metastases shrank, it was good news. If they were stable, it was not-so-bad news. But, God forbid, if metastases were progressing, it was bad news. Thus, the tests had an immediate prognostic value. Without exaggeration, patients and their moral support expected the results of recently performed diagnostic tests with trembling hearts.

Once in a polite and gentle manner, we asked our doctor to inform us about the results of the tests at the end of the day when they were taken, but to our disappointment, she kept us in suspense until we saw her for the next scheduled visit. We were probably not the only ones who asked her to inform them about the results sooner, but she responded with polite silence and would not change her policy. Because of this attitude, during visits when we expected to hear about Marina's diagnostic imaging test results, we were filled with anxiety, which could be avoided. Maybe the most plausible explanation for Dr. Miller's policy was that she did not want to startle a patient over the phone with an alarming result. Being impeccably effective in comforting her patients, she possibly thought that if the results were bad, she would rather talk with the patient face-to-face in an effort to convince the patient that the situation was not as bad as it seemed.

Questions and Answers

As in the past, during Marina's reprieve while receiving Faslodex, again blinded by unquenchable hope, I naïvely asked Dr. Miller about the possibility of having CT and body scans on a less frequent than quarterly basis. In response, I received a condescending smile on her beautiful, benevolent face. Dr. Miller correctly perceived my question to be childish. Only when the cancer unexpectedly raised its ugly face once more did I understand the whole meaning of her silence.

All things considered, Marina was happy with her new oncologist. Dr. Miller successfully kept our hope that it was too early to worry about the worst outcome. Demonstrating sincere interest in Marina's health, she did not avoid our questions. Comparing her with the experiences we'd had with earlier physicians, we knew we were in good hands. Like numerous physicians we'd met before, she was good at explaining the signs and symptoms of the current stage, but like the majority of physicians we met, she rarely, if ever, talked about the place of the specific symptom in the global picture of the disease. At the end of each visit, the receptionist handed Marina several printed pages of information that summarized the visit. Unfortunately, these pages provided patients with minimal information about what was going on with them strategically and did not say broadly what was the place of the new, if there was, symptom in the overall picture of the illness. In addition, like majority of physicians whom we met, Dr. Miller hardly ever discussed possible major side effects of the ordered medications.

Based on the experience learned by Marina and me, the only good way to be an informed patient is to not hesitate to ask questions to the doctor. These questions a patient asks must be carefully thought out before the visit. Ever since Marina and I discovered this effective method of obtaining necessary information, in anticipation of our next appointment, we composed a list of questions to ask the doctor. Being busy with their numerous obligations, physicians must follow the time schedule of appointments, but no matter how busy the doctors are, or how much they are in a hurry to see the next patient, they have no other choice but to listen to and answer legitimate questions presented to them by a patient. As observed in most cases, at the end of a visit while ready to leave, while doctors answer questions, with their body language, they let the patient know they are in a hurry. No one argues that doctors have legitimate priorities, but so do the patients who need to leave the office with all their questions answered.

Silent Revolution in the Provision of Medical Care in the United States

In April 2014, Marina developed a severe abdominal pain that was apparently not related to her cancer, for which she was admitted to a hospital located not far from the suburb where we lived. In the ER, a doctor asked her some general questions, and after a superficial examination, he sent her for a CT scan. After receiving the results of the tests, he came back to Marina's ER room and announced that he was discharging her home giving the reason "you are not obstructed." An ordinary patient will not be able to understand this phrase, but as a physician, I understood that Marina's gastrointestinal tract was not blocked. Marina objected to being discharged, telling the doctor that although she'd received an injection of morphine, she still had a severe stomachache. That finally persuaded the physician to admit her to the hospital for observation and treatment. Over the next two days, Marina's abdominal pain gradually subsided, and her repeated CT scan was again negative for obstruction, which meant that she was ready to be discharged from the hospital.

During this short, favorable hospital visit, I made a very important unpleasant observation that I confirmed later when I myself happened to be a patient in two different hospitals. A new phenomenon in American medicine that I discovered was the wide replacement of primary care physicians, who not long ago were providing hospital care for their patients, with inpatient physicians or hospitalists. Hospitalists are hired by administration of a hospital and treat patients who are admitted for diagnosis and treatment. This silent revolution in patient medical care has happened over the past twenty years or so, and although it is portrayed on some TV medical shows, it is still widely unknown to the public. As a result of this radical change, the management of many patients in hospitals was given up, mostly voluntarily, by physicians' groups and patients' primary physicians and were turned over to the hospitalists. On a personal level, I have absolutely no complaints about hospitalists. Like other American doctors, they are highly educated, highly professional, and have good manners. They are hardly the problem. The problem is the new style of delivery system of medical care in America where private doctors are often excluded from the provision of medical care. If between a primary doctor and patient, sooner or later, develops a degree of emotional bonding, a typical hospitalist is free from forming an emotional connection with any patient.

From my firsthand experience, it became clear that it is usually a waste of time to expect the same quality of relationship with a hospitalist as with a primary physician. While the primary physicians are inherently interested in retaining their patients, for hospitalists, that is not an issue—the hospital setting guarantees them a constant influx of patients. In cases where a patient is dissatisfied with their primary physician, they can change a doctor, but that is practically impossible and does not make much sense with a hospitalist.

Although the main responsibility of hospitalists is toward their patients, in reality whether want it or not, their main allegiance belongs to the hospital that hired them, and indirectly to the insurance company that pays the hospital's bills. Significant number of hospitalists are working on the relatively short duration contracts and these contracts can be easily cancelled by the hospital. When a patient is admitted to a hospital, one of the main goals of the hospitalist is to follow the rules of the insurance company. This allows the hospital to achieve its best economic interest—mainly to save money—by discharging the patient in a timely manner, corresponding to insurance company's policies. Each twelve-hour shift brings to patients a different hospitalist, who rightfully so cannot understand who after all their primary medical care provider is.

Traditionally, most people prefer to be taken care of by their primary doctor who in many respects are widely independent in their medical decisions. No wonder former President Obama, when he presented the benefits of his Affordable Care Act, promised on several occasions that with this new system, the patient would keep their own personal physician. For most hospitalists, despite their best efforts, patients are seen in a two-dimensional way and known only by a last name and a superficial knowledge of their medical history. In many cases, patients have a long, complicated history of not one but several health conditions, which--despite all expectations of health organizers and all the sincere wishes of hospitalists--are impossible to understand completely.

The problem of communication between a patient and their primary doctor has become much more complicated after a patient is hospitalized. When primary physicians or medical groups give up their professional privileges to provide hospital care, they surrender to hospitalists the right to make all medical decisions for their patients. The most that a primary physician can then do to serve their patients when they are hospitalized is--if they want--to visit them personally in the hospital; however, they do not have rights to make any medical decisions for their patients. That's how private physicians, who are patients' medical care conductors, became "semiconductors" of medical care.

A patient who is hospitalized requires more professional skills in the management of their health condition than an outpatient. Many highly trained primary physicians gave up the management of their hospitalized patients based on such conveniences as not being called to the hospital for emergencies, not being awakened in the middle of the night, and limiting the possibility to potential medical malpractice suits. Due to the gravity of the patient's health condition, during the hospitalization, the risk of a malpractice suit is higher when the patient is in the hospital as compared with an outpatient setting. The outcome of the decision by many primary physicians to delegate hospital care to the hospitalists has meant a dramatic change, often resulting in the loss of their medical proficiency in the potential management of their hospitalized patients.

During Marina's hospital stay for stomach pain, each day she was examined by a different hospitalist. Almost all of them were young, handsome, and polite, but the communication with them, the warmth, encouragement, and compassion, traditionally expected with a primary physician, was absent, or better to say did not exist. The unspoken message from the hospitalist was "I am your doctor today, and I will do my best to provide you excellent service, but, please, do not try to establish personal bridges . . . we both have our privacy, so let's respect it. Do not expect me to be personal and show sympathy for your condition; that is not my function. I am here to treat your body, not your spirit. If you need spiritual help, I will be glad to refer you to a mental care provider."

When Marina was discharged by a hospitalist, she never saw her before, she asked her what her final diagnosis was. The hospitalist looked at her, not hiding her surprise. She could not understand why the patient would be interested in such "a medical thing" as final diagnosis. Her answer was as vague as the diagnosis. After thinking a little, she told Marina that her diagnosis was "idiopathic abdominal pain." Notwithstanding that such a diagnosis could be made by a child, the doctor let Marina figure out for herself the possible cause for her abdominal pain.

Marina repeated the same question.

"There are many reasons for abdominal pain," the doctor replied. "In your case, it was nothing dramatic. With your gastrointestinal reflux, GERD, for which you are already being treated, I'll bet the pain was related to your diet. Main thing you were not obstructed."

"If, as you told me in the beginning, I do not need additional medication then what should I do to avoid another hospitalization?" Marina asked.

"Well," the doctor answered, "I can have a nutritionist speak to you before you are discharged. She will give you instructions about your diet."

"Why not you, Doctor?"

"Because she is the specialist in that area."

The dietitian soon arrived with a small stack of instructions that she had photocopied from books. She handed them to Marina and recommended that she read the material attentively.

Marina was lucky that her husband was a physician who, after analyzing the details of the illness, understood that the reason for Marina's abdominal pain was recently developed lactose intolerance. Since then, lactose containing products were eliminated and the abdominal pain disappeared. Very simple.

Optimists Do Not Give Up

A substantial setback in Marina's illness took place in May 2015, eighteen months after the Faslodex therapy started and ten years after her cancer was diagnosed. She was seventy-two years at the time. Dr. Miller informed Marina that on her recent imaging studies, while other metastases were stable, she had noticed there was a slight increase in the number of metastases in the liver. As a result, the doctor stopped Faslodex and replaced it with a proven combination of two drugs, Letrozole and Ibrance. Dr. Miller assured us that she expected good results in response to this therapy.

Letrozole, or Femara, is a nonsteroidal aromatase inhibitor that lowers the body's estrogen production. Ibrance was a drug from which much was expected, having been recently introduced in oncological practice at the time. According to medical research articles and news media, it was supposed to have a great potential to improve cancer treatment. Ibrance was one of the first medications of its class that affected the body's immune system, enhancing its ability to resist the growth of cancer cells. Unfortunately, the problem with Ibrance was that, as with all other classes of anticancer medications, with time and after going through mutations, breast cancer cells become largely immune to anticancer drugs.

Marina was a good soldier. She accepted each new cycle in her anticancer treatment as a blessing from God and was now ready to start the new treatment. Along with rational thinking, I continued to believe that Marina could be an exception to the laws of nature and having been greatly encouraged by the preceding favorable eighteen months of treatment with Faslodex, I had an expectation that the new, innovative drug combination would provide a similar, if not an even better, response. Still ignoring the unmitigated aggression of Marina's cancerous tumor cells, I created for myself a wrong impression, that for Marina to continue to live with cancer, the only thing necessary was to tolerate the new anticancer medication prescribed to her. Such was the strength of my hope that after ten years of Marina's disease, I still could not be convinced of the formidable capacity of cancerous cells to overcome all attempts to get rid of them.

Meanwhile, fighting for her life, Marina remained an exemplary patient. She hardly ever missed a diagnostic test, appointment, or treatment procedure. She was exemplary not because she clung to life, but because she was doing it not only for herself but--admitted by her--for her responsibility toward her family.

Orthopedic Disagreements

After Marina had been receiving the promised-to-be-effective Letrozole and Ibrance combination for two months, she developed pain in her right hip.

Initially it was a dull pain, but with each new day, the pain became more intense. Her bone pain could be a bad prognostic sign, because for years, Marina's long bones had been stuffed with cancerous metastases that could make the skeleton fragile and brittle, prone to pains and fractures. We were both nervous, since the hip pain could signal that Marina might have a hip fracture. Like most people, Marina and I disliked going to the doctor without good reason, but the pain in her hip got worse every day, so in the end, we went to see an orthopedic surgeon, Dr. Lazar. I had known Dr. Lazar for many years and was on friendly terms with him. The many patients that I had referred to him had always been satisfied with his services. Besides being a doctor, he was a talented writer of nonfiction books, where he reflected on the numerous challenges of medical practice in the sphere of orthopedics.

Before visiting Dr. Lazar, Marina requested by phone that his office nurse give her a referral for a hip X-ray, but to her pleasant surprise, the nurse told her there was an X-ray machine in Dr. Lazar's office, so there was no need to go to the X-ray department.

What followed is a good example that we should be aware that nobody, including doctors, could be perfect. When American physicians inform their patients of the small details of their condition, as a rule, they do not enlighten the patients about the importance of this or that symptom, or of a specific finding in a lab test within the general picture of the disease. Of course, this would not happen if such doctors simply respected more the intelligence of their patients.

Judging by the number of people in the waiting room, Dr. Lazar seemed a popular orthopedic surgeon. The nurse led Marina to the exam room and took her vital signs and history, and then a radiology technician came in to take Marina to the X-ray room.

When x-ray films were quickly completed, to the exam room entered Dr. Lazar, accompanied by a scribe who had with her iPad to document the visit. Doctor warmly greeted us and started examining Marina. After that, he turned on the X-ray viewer, where the scribe previously placed the X-ray films and began to study them. The more he looked at the films, the more his face assumed an expression of concern.

Eventually he turned to Marina. "Well, Marina, it appears that we have a real problem," he said in an alarmed tone of voice. "The inside space of both of your femurs, especially on the left side, is packed with metastatic changes all the way up to the femoral head. Looking at your films, I am afraid that at any moment you could develop a fracture of one or both of your femurs. The X-ray study certainly goes along with the pain you are experiencing. I am quite surprised that with all the bone metastases, you did not have pain in your legs even long time ago. I see on the X-ray films that that the inner space of sides of your long bones are thinning out with secondary microfractures and I am afraid not so much about your bones' microfractures but of the real possibility you might develop a full fracture of the bone. If that occurs at the level of the femur head, it presents a major problem. For now, I recommend you walk as little as possible and as gently as you can. All this said, the last word in the decision about your further management should belong to an orthopedic surgeon who specializes in the field of oncology. My nurse will give you the contact information for the specialist I recommend. He deals with problems like yours daily, and he will give you a more definite opinion about the issues. Meanwhile, Marina, please be careful and walk as little as possible. If you don't have a choice then apply weight on your legs as gently as possible. At least until you see the specialist, I recommend that you use a walker when you walk. If the specialist thinks you need a wheelchair, I am sure Medicare covers this expense. Let me know what he tells you."

Marina, who usually reacted to sad news much better than I did, was much less affected by these results than I was. When things did not go the way we expected, she often reminded me of a parable by the famous American-Armenian writer William Saroyan. In this parable, a king orders a carpenter to deliver to him an impossibly huge amount of sawdust the next day; otherwise, the carpenter is going to lose his head. Desperate, the carpenter returns home. His friend, also a carpenter, tells him to stop crying and forget what will happen. The carpenter and his family eat, drink, sing, and dance all night. But when the morning comes, the family is in tears. It appears that the carpenter's downfall is inevitable. At the appointed hour, they hear knocking at the door. The carpenter opens the door, ready for the worst.

"Carpenter," says king's man, "the king is dead. Go to the palace and build him a coffin."

The Russian expression *"Не говори гоп пока не перепрыгнешь,"* or "Don't say hop until you jump over," which in English correlates with "Don't count your chickens before they are hatched."

Unlike me, who imagined Marina to soon be a bedridden invalid, she, following her motto to live one day at a time, also followed Hippocrates's recommendation "Let food be thy medicine." On the way home, she told me that she was hungry and asked me to take her to the closest restaurant.

Entering our home, I at once called the oncologic orthopedic surgeon's office to arrange an appointment for Marina. The secretary gave us an appointment in three days. Then I went to a medical supply pharmacy and bought a walker, which was supposed to reduce the risk of a leg fracture. In addition, I got information about either renting or buying a wheelchair in the future.

With Marina leaning on the walker and me holding her by her elbow, on the day of the scheduled appointment, we entered the university's orthopedic surgery clinic. First registering at the front desk, we took seats facing the waiting room desk. Over many years of visiting different physicians, we had gotten used to being patient in the role of patients. For example, sometimes like other patients, we waited an hour or longer to be called in to a busy physician's exam room. In the beginning, I would become tense after a half hour of waiting, but with time, I realized that being nervous and impatient only harmed me and did not do any good. On that day, there were many patients in the waiting room, so Marina and I prepared for a long wait. However, this time we were wrong. We did not know there were many doctors who worked in that same unit. Even more important and surprising was that the flow of patients was under the strict control of one of the physicians. It was the first and the last time I ever saw that a doctor, in this case a stocky man in his early sixties dressed like a gentleman under his lab coat, periodically appeared at the reception desk to make sure patients were not waiting too long for their physician. Checking the charts, peering into the faces of patients, and addressing clerks, he reminded me of a military commander on the battleground.

The unit was well organized and ran like clockwork. Exactly at the time of the scheduled appointment, a nurse called Marina. As usual, I was with her for moral support. We got to the exam room, and right away the nurse took Marina's vital signs. When she was about to leave, Marina handed her an envelope with the X-rays taken at Dr. Lazar's office. The nurse took the envelope but said the doctor only trusted X-rays taken in his own office. She left us, and a technician came in and took Marina for the X-ray study. It took only ten minutes for her to return. Soon a fellow in orthopedic surgery came in, bringing the new X-ray films with her. She listened attentively to Marina's complaints, examined her, and left the exam room, promising that her boss would come soon. Accompanied by the medical fellow, the oncologic orthopedic surgeon, Professor Diamandis, appeared almost immediately. We instantly recognized the physician who was at the waiting room to make sure the schedule of appointments was being strictly followed.

He greeted us, and having a short conversation with the fellow, he walked over to the X-ray viewer and began to examine the films. Both Marina and I held our breath, waiting for what Professor Diamandis will say. Will he confirm the recommendation of Dr. Lazar to walk as little as possible unless using a walker or a wheelchair? Or will he make even the worse recommendation, that she should not be on her feet most of a time?

Unable to restrain herself, Marina broke the silence and asked in a voice trembling with tension, "Doctor Diamandis, tell me please, will I ever be able to walk?"

Knowing well how important his answer was for us, the doctor turned toward Marina and not showing any emotion asked, not hiding his curiosity, "Why did you decide that you are not going to walk?"

"The doctor that referred us to you told us so," Marina answered.

"Well, you should not worry. You can walk without any restriction," the professor told us to our amazement.

"Why do you say so, Doctor?" Marina said in a strained voice.

"Because the metastatic lesions in your legs do not compromise the strength of your bones."

"Then why did our orthopedic surgeon, whom we deeply respect, scare me so much?"

"If he had been sure of his conclusion, he would not have referred you to me. I repeat, you do not have any more predisposition for fractures than a normal person, and you may continue to walk without limitations. Your leg pain is not related to the metastases, and you can take over-the-counter medications for it," Professor Diamandis said with a serious expression on his face, ready to leave.

"If you don't mind, Professor, one more thing, please. Is there anything you can recommend for my back pain? It bothers me usually in the morning?" Marina asked.

"Well, I specialize in problems with hips and legs. For a qualified answer about your back, you should go to Dr. Chapman," professor said, not hiding his annoyance with a type of question he no doubt had heard many times before and left the room.

So much for modern specialization. Already in 1880, the famous Russian author Fyodor Dostoyevsky in his book *The Brothers Karamazov* prophetically foresaw a time when the left nostril would be treated by a specialist in Paris and the right nostril by a different specialist in Vienna.

No doubt Professor Diamandis was a talented physician. Thanks to him Marina received a ticket to continue to lead a normal way of life, helping her use her both legs for walking rather than becoming an appendage to a walker. It was unfortunate that like many doctors, he did not explain the reason for his impression. Like many physicians, with all his virtues ignoring their patients' intelligence, he failed to make clear the reason of his opinion in a few words, which was basically the same thing as ordering insulin to a patient with diabetes and not explaining to the patient why and how insulin is given.

Luckily, I was a doctor, and I knew that the advice given to Marina was based on the fact that there are two types of bone metastases: osteoclastic, characterized by the destruction of normal bone, and osteoblastic (or sclerotic), characterized by the deposition of new bone. Metastatic bone lesions could be either osteoblastic or osteoclastic. Unlike osteoclastic metastases that weaken bone, osteoblastic metastases do not have that effect. Looking at Marina's X-ray films, Professor Diamandis, without difficulty, recognized that Marina's bone metastases were of the osteoblastic type. It was surprising why what was so easy for Diamandis to see on the X-ray, by some reason, misled my good friend Dr. Lazar. Another confirmation that medicine is not only a science but also an art.

On the way home, Marina was jubilant that my good friend Dr. Lazar's judgment was wrong and that she could return to normal walking. It remains only to add that metastatic invasion of major bones usually produces pain and broken bones, but thankfully, Marina never had this type of complication.

When I called Dr. Lazar and told him about the visit, he congratulated me on the result.

Visit to a Gastroenterologist

The life of a patient with advanced cancer is full of unpleasant developments. Two weeks after our visit to Professor Diamandis, Marina's leg pain disappeared, but she began to experience severe heartburn caused either by chemotherapy drugs, or her illness, or both. Over-the-counter remedies such as Tums, Mylanta, and baking soda did not help, so Dr. Miller referred her to a gastroenterologist. Following the unwritten rule, a cancer patient has the privilege of being able to get an appointment with a specialist in the shortest possible time. Marina got an appointment with a GI the very next day.

The doctor's office was comfortable and spacious. At the scheduled time, Marina and I were called to the exam room. As usual, a nurse took Marina's vital signs and asked about her symptoms. The door had just closed behind the nurse when the gastroenterologist entered the room, carrying in his extended hands an open laptop. Putting it in on the table, and without taking his eyes from its screen, he muttered words of greeting, and still not looking at us at least once, he began to ask his own questions.

With the introduction of a computer into daily medical routines, communication between the examining physician and the patient drastically changed compared to how they were from the time immemorial. As it is known, a human being can really concentrate on one task at a time: it is either the patient or the computer. However, during an appointment, nowadays the primary attention of many physicians is divided between talking with a patient and simultaneously entering notes into a computer. A physician focused on writing a progress note cuts down on eye contact with the patient, which inevitably creates an impression that typing into the computer is more important than interacting with the patient. A written record is important, but an inadequately collected medical history from the actual patient might result in ordering unnecessary tests and making inaccurate recommendations. I saw it many times that doctors formed their own quick impression of what the patient suffers from a priori and then directed the patient's responses in a way that confirms the presumed by them imagined diagnosis.

Several minutes passed during which the gastroenterologist, whose head was hidden behind the laptop's lid, still had not honored Marina with a single glance. It was possible that he had somehow already noticed her, while the lid of the computer obstructed his field of his vision. In the good old days when computers did not become yet an integral part of modern life, a patient could legitimately complain that the physician "did not even look at me during the visit," but now the doctors can complain that in addition to talking to the patient, they must also write electronic medical record of the visit. Though we had gotten used to a computer in the medical office long ago as an object being an obstacle between physician and patient, finally the distance separating us from this doctor became so intolerable for Marina that first glancing at me, she took a deep breath and resolutely and in a loud voice said, "Doctor, I'm very sorry, but this is just impossible. Why didn't you look at me at least once? I am not a mannequin but a human being after all!"

I had expected a defensive reaction from the doctor, but that did not happen. It turned out that the doctor knew very well that eye contact with the patient was a vital part of a visit.

"Please, forgive me," he said apologetically. "I do not like this new work-style either, but my administration requires physicians to provide an electronic record of each appointment. I need to see fifteen more patients today, so to be on time, I must save every minute possible. Usually, patients do not complain as you so rightly did, but I know that I am wrong. However, if I do not enter the information now, while my wife protests, I will need to do it at home before I go to sleep, and I might forget necessary details to this moment. I promise to be better in the future."

The end of the visit was delightful. The doctor was a sensitive person who did his best to satisfy the interests of his patients. With a smile on his young handsome face, he closed the lid of the computer, and now, taking notes in his notebook, he maintained eye contact with Marina when she talked. At the end of the visit, the doctor explained what we already knew, that her heartburn could be the result of chemotherapy, cancer, or a combination of both.

"I am going to prescribe a proton ion pump inhibitor for you," he said in conclusion. "Regardless of the nature of your heartburn, this medication should help, together with changes to your diet, of which you will learn about from a pamphlet my nurse will give you before you leave."

The new medication helped Marina with her heartburn, though it was not always effective against the pain produced by the aggressive cancer.

Dermatologist's Disappointment

Like any involved caregiver, I tried everything possible to help Marina on the difficult path of her ordeal. Being sick did not prevent her from fulfilling her from, inherent in her strong spousal commitment, keeping an eye on me. Moved by love, she wanted me to look good. Once, inspecting my face, she noticed a bump on the top of my head that had recently appeared, which except for a slight itch did not bother me a bit. On the third week of this finding, Marina began to insist that I needed to be seen by a dermatologist. As it usually happened, I refused initially, but who can resist the pressure of a loving wife?

The dermatologist, with an excellent reputation, a pleasant woman, used a magnifying glass to examine my lesion. A magnifying glass in hands of the dermatologist is the same as a stethoscope on the neck of an internist. After a minute of careful scrutiny, she announced firmly that I had basal cell carcinoma. Obviously, she was so confident in her diagnosis that without hesitation she scheduled me for the surgical removal of my lesion in two weeks. Knowing that this type of cancer responds well to treatment, I was not scared. Moreover, following my tendency of finding good in bad, I began to ponder what good I could find in this situation. Before leaving the dermatologist's office and receiving another unpleasant assurance by the dermatologist that I had skin cancer, I hurried home.

When I got home, I informed Marina with a radiant look that now we both had cancer, and therefore we were comrades in misfortune. I thought my gesture was the same as when a spouse of a bald cancer patient shaves his hair in solidarity. I knew beforehand that Marina would not react positively to my news, but why not try? The undisputable fact was I had cancer; therefore, now we were comrades in arms.

No matter how Marina reacted to my news, to my disappointment, in several days, my alleged cancerous tumor began to shrink slightly and peel off. That persisted until the lesion practically disappeared. Marina, who had not shown any satisfaction from my solidarity with her condition, congratulated me on the good news and suggested I cancel the next appointment to the dermatologist. That day being in the hospital for other business, I went to the skin doctor's office to tell there that I "recovered from cancer," and do not need the surgery anymore.

The nurse from the dermatologist's office with whom I spoke disagreed adamantly with my decision. "If our doctor told you your lesion is malignant, it is malignant. My doctor never makes mistakes," she said emphatically, smiling at me patronizingly.

"But I do not feel the lesion anymore, and it is not there," I tried to object.

"That doesn't mean anything. It's just under your skin now," she explained to me.

Knowing that at least the tumor should be somehow visible, I wanted to object, but I decided not to argue with the enlightened assistant to the expert.

At the designated time, I came for the appointed visit and was examined by my dermatologist and her assistant. "Doctor, great news," I said seeing her when she appeared on the threshold. "My lesion has disappeared. Hooray! Luckily, I don't have cancer."

Not showing any reaction, the dermatologist approached me with a decisive step. She pulled out a legendary magnifying glass from her pocket and began to carefully examine the place where I was supposed to have cancer. Several tense minutes passed until she put aside her magnifying glass back in her pocket and then, not hiding her professional disappointment and not sharing my justified joy, she took a deep breath and uttered with a deep regret, "Really, I cannot see anything."

Was she upset because she had made a mistake in her diagnosis, or because I had disrupted the surgery schedule, I don't know. But for obvious reasons, I did not share her frustration; I did not have skin cancer and could not become Marina's friend in misfortune.

The most intriguing feature of this story is that it is completely true: my dermatologist was disappointed that I did not have cancer. It happens sometimes.

Hope Is the Nourishment of the Soul

Letrozole and Ibrance combination was effective for Marina for fifteen months, from May 2015 until October 2016. Despite many previous failures with different drugs, once again forgetting about the past experience, during these months Marina and I believed we had finally found the magic bullet that would keep her cancer under control for a long time. I dreamed that she would easily tolerate the next drug, conveniently forgetting that with time, cancer inventively creates mutations that allow it to resist chemo. Remarkable was that my irrational expectation did not present anything unusual in human relations. Hope is a powerful feeling that keeps people alive and at peace with themselves. Instead of worrying, Marina constantly found something important to do to distract herself from dark thoughts.

Being afraid with a possibility that the cancer progressed, our trips to the oncologist's office were nervous when we expected to hear from the doctor the results of the recent imaging studies. However, when Marina was in decent shape and when we were not anxious about receiving bad news, our trips down the Road of Hope were relaxing and delightful.

Marina did not allow the illness to bend her will to live, and she did everything that was necessary to maintain the semblance of a normal life. All the way back in 2006, when she had just finished her initial treatment, she had resumed her dance class and walking, either outdoors in our neighborhood or at the local fitness club. In 2012, when after five years of reprieve, she experienced a recurrence of the cancer, her physical exercise routine depended on the particular chemotherapy treatment she received. As a rule, she was ready to resume physical exercise on the third or fourth day after having the chemo, though her condition periodically required her to stop physical exercise. Her favorite exercise remained walking.

In 2015, Marina was forced to stop walking because of her lack of energy. However, that did not prevent her from doing all the household tasks such as shopping, cooking, laundry, and many more. The housecleaning was done by a professional cleaning service every two weeks. Marina did her household chores slower than before, but she insisted that no one help her. Whenever her condition allowed, she went to the fitness club, where her exercise of choice became an aquatics class. Sometimes she used a treadmill, walking on it with minimal speed, but she walked.

Power of Love

Marina never missed being with our grandchildren, which by far remained her favorite activity. She took these happy opportunities very seriously, and days beforehand, she was preparing to ensure their time together would be interesting and exciting.

On the morning of a wonderful July day in 2016 when Marina had just finished a Letrozole and Ibrance treatment cycle, we picked up Ariel and Ruthie from their home, and having a delightful breakfast at a cafeteria, we drove to downtown Chicago. First, we spent time at Chicago's Millennium Park, where the children had a lot to do and see. After a few hours, Ariel suggested that we all go to take the Chicago boat tour. As usual, his older sister strongly supported him. Before leaving Millennium Park, we visited an ice cream parlor, and after a delightful hour there, walked toward the Chicago River boat rides. From the moment we reached Upper Wacker Drive, where the boat tour stations were located, I felt tired. By now it was noon, with the sun high in the sky and the weather hot and humid, and to reach the boat station we, still, had to walk a good distance. Holding the children's hands, Marina, as if she were a young person, was walking easily and briskly while I dragged behind the group. Despite all my efforts, the distance between us increased with each minute. By the time I reached the boat station, Marina and the children had already been there for a while.

"Grandpa, what's the matter with you?" Ruthie asked me. "Why are you slow as a turtle today? We have been here for three minutes waiting for you."

As I muttered something in my defense, it dawned on me that I had just witnessed a true miracle. Marina, who had received her chemo treatment just five days ago and who only yesterday had needed to spend hours to restore her energy, was full of vitality and strength today. There could be only one explanation to this transformation. In the presence of the grandchildren she loved so much, Marina, who was supposed to be tired and slow, had before my eyes became full of energy and a physically strong woman. Love for children, and her wish to make everything good for them inspired her to such a degree that it had a powerful spiritual effect on her. Instead of seeing a woman being physically affected by continued cycles of chemotherapy, the grandchildren and I saw before us a perfectly healthy woman.

As it could be expected, the incredible transformation with Marina did not last long. As soon as the children left us, her fatigue and lack of energy returned as it were before. This sultry summer day was the last time in Marina's life when she was able to be so energetic and strong. Only her deep love for her grandchildren was able to produce that incredible miracle.

The Battle Resumes

In August 2016, Marina's cancer cells won their seventh victory, this time over the latest chemo medications, Letrozole and Ibrance, for which we'd had such elevated expectations. Though Marina had suffered another defeat, we felt grateful that at least these medications had successfully controlled the growth of her metastases for an entire fifteen months. It was her liver, and to a lesser degree, her lungs, where new aggressive cancerous cells became unresponsive to the current treatment. Especially disappointing was that Ibrance, venerated in media as one of the first medications of its class that affected the body's immune system, was powerless in the fight against her cancer.

Though three years ago, Abraxane had produced such a strong negative influence on Marina's health that Dr. Arnold then had been ready to send my wife for hospice--a sad and unforgivable decision--our present oncologist, Dr. Debra Miller, decided to restart this medication. When Marina questioned her about the possibility that Abraxane would again strongly disagree with her health, Dr. Miller, who most likely knew something we did not know, reassured Marina that she knew what she was doing. Trying to not have doubts, we refrained from additional questioning. Who knows, maybe Dr. Miller ordered Abraxane for Marina simply because she was running out of other options?

It was mid-September in 2016 when, at the age of seventy-three, Marina again began to experience respiratory symptoms in addition to fatigue and sleepiness. She did not think it was a reaction to Abraxane but, rather, a viral infection. That same day, we visited our primary physician, internist Dr. Richard Sittam. Highly professional and compassionate, Dr. Sittam had taken care of Marina's general health for twenty years. Based on his examination and the lab finding that she had low levels of red blood cells and hemoglobin, he recommended that she be admitted to the hospital.

The next day, after receiving intravenous fluids, Marina's condition improved only slightly, and she continued to be very ill. One of the reasons why her condition was bad was her worsened anemia. Another day passed, and after lab tests and X-rays, Dr. Sittam concluded that Marina's problem was not a respiratory infection but an unfavorable reaction to Abraxane. When he contacted Dr. Miller, she told him that until Marina was in the hospital, it was okay to stop Abraxane temporarily. During his evening rounds on the second day, Dr. Sittam told Marina that in his experience, cancer patients with anemia could benefit from a blood transfusion. Though a blood transfusion is usually recommended when the level of hemoglobin drops to six grams per deciliter, and Marina's level was close to eight grams per deciliter, he believed Marina needed this procedure. The next day, he consulted Dr. Miller, who at first was hesitant but eventually agreed with him.

To make sure Marina would tolerate the blood transfusion, her doctor ordered several tests. Started early in the evening, blood transfusion was performed by a floor nurse and lasted for several hours. The next day when I went to Marina's hospital room, I could not believe my eyes. It was a miracle. Her condition had improved to such a degree that she was active and alert, and best of all, she was smiling. She tolerated the blood transfusion without complications, and indeed the procedure had done the trick. As if nothing special had happened, Marina ignored my compliments about her condition's improvement. It was typical for her to avoid talking about her health. According to her, everything was now normal, and all she wanted presently was to continue to enjoy life. The next day, she was safely discharged from the hospital.

The Gastrointestinal Tract Challenges

The life of a patient with metastatic cancer is never boring and, unfortunately, often it is challenging. It sounds paradoxical, but besides diarrhea,
chemotherapy medications can cause constipation. Marina had already
showed her predisposition to constipation in the middle of her illness, and
the symptom now continued to worsen. Once when a new chemotherapy
drug was introduced, she had a severe episode of bowel irregularity. Since
then, she had periodically experienced difficulty emptying her intestinal
tract, and gradually she was becoming more and more prone to this unpleasant symptom. In the initial stages of constipation, she had successfully
taken care of the problem using popular laxatives like Senokot, Colace, or
Dulcolax. The problem was progressively worsening, and Marina consulted with different specialists who in one voice told her that her constipation
was a side effect of chemotherapy.

Over-the-counter laxatives are classified as bulk forming, stool softeners, intestinal lubricants, saline laxatives, enemas, and stimulants. For mild
to moderate constipation, Marina used stool softeners. However, despite
taking the laxative from time to time, her constipation lasted for several
days. Following the unanimous advice of physicians, she began to use strong
stimulant laxatives. Each time she took them, she eventually had a bowel
movement, but she paid a dear price in pain for the achieved result. Over
the years, Marina went through many of these agonizingly painful episodes.
Such is the prose of life that usually extremely modest with anybody--includ-
ing me--in sharing information about her bodily functions, she suffered
from excruciating abdominal pain, during which she was forced moaning,
crying, and occasionally loudly yelling because of abdominal spasms. This
unbearable pain could last for hours.

It is impossible for me to forget how Marina suffered from these episodes. Like a defeated warrior, she lay on the bathroom floor, motionless
with her eyes closed, tired, drained, and still moaning from pain. Why God
would allow such torment to be suffered by millions of innocent souls will
remain for me an unresolvable puzzle.

Knowing that most people tolerate stimulant laxatives perfectly well without having such a painful reaction, I shared with my colleagues how my wife reacted to them, but they just shrugged in disbelief and continued to recommend the same treatment for her constipation, not realizing that they were making a serious mistake. Eventually, during another painful episode of prolonged and excruciating constipation, I had a good idea. I recalled that, as a rule, patients preparing for colonoscopy received large doses of the stool softener MiraLAX and hardly anybody experienced any side effects. MiraLAX softens and eases stools by gently attracting water into the colon through osmosis. Obtaining a jar of MiraLAX in the pharmacy, I gave Marina a large dose of it, just as if she were preparing for a colonoscopy. The result was stunning. No pain, no suffering, no irregularity. Finally, we had found the magic bullet to control her irregularity. The cheap, effective remedy had resolved the symptom.

It took several years before I understood what the cause of Marina's painful reaction to stimulant laxatives was. Marina's visits to the oncology clinic interspersed with visits to two nurse practitioners who worked in conjunction with Dr. Miller. During one of such visits, the nurse practitioner asked Marina if she had abdominal problems that, as it was known, often happened with the chemo drug that Marina took. Marina told her that presently she took MiraLAX that helped her but in the past she had very bad, painful reactions when she was taking stimulating laxatives. Luckily, after she began using MiraLAX, there were no more problems. "I do not have any idea why I had such a strange reaction to stimulating laxatives," she concluded.

The nurse practitioner looked at Marina and smiled knowingly. "Unfortunately, it is more than expected that you had pain attacks when you took this type of laxatives," she said.

"My mother had lymphoma," the nurse practitioner answered, "and we had the same problem with her chronic constipation and with her agonizing pain when she took laxatives to stimulate her bowels. She suffered severely and nobody could explain us what was going on until we visited an experienced internist and explained to him what was going on with my mother. The internist responded that he treated couple of similar cases in his practice.

"According to what he told us, there was nothing surprising about my mother's reaction to stimulating laxatives," the nurse practitioner continued. "For a patient like my mother and now like you, Marina, it would be surprising if you would not have constipation and would not have severe pain after taking stimulant laxatives. The constipation and abdominal pain that you, Marina, experienced was because after many years of your disease besides other location of metastases you also have metastases in your gastrointestinal system. These metastases are responsible both for constipation and for the pain you experienced when you were taking stimulant laxatives. These stimulant laxatives produce a strong peristalsis of the bowel musculature, forcing the content of bowels to push against the intestinal segments where there are metastatic obstructions. Result of this is the agonizing pain that you were experiencing. Obviously, the doctors with whom you consulted did not realize that your main condition is metastatic cancer and that in its advanced stage, it can create bowel obstructions."

It turns out that all the highly educated, many times certified American specialists with whom Marina consulted unanimously ignored a possibility of frequently present partial bowel obstructions in the patient with the metastatic cancer. Once again, I learned that doctors are not perfect, and I was one of them as well. As the Latin saying goes, *Dum habitas discite*—While you live, learn.

Light of Hope for the Future. Life without Vasomotor Hot Flashes. Piglet and Winnie-the-Pooh.

At the end of October 2016, Marina's quarterly CT and bone scans revealed further growth of metastases in her lungs and liver. Though this time Abraxane did not produce significant side effects, it again proved to be ineffective against her cancerous cells. It needed to be replaced with another chemotherapeutic agent. Once again, we were reminded that despite all the numerous promising scientific achievements in the treatment of cancer, a "magic bullet" for treatment of cancer still did not exist.

In November 2016, Dr. Miller discontinued Abraxane and prescribed chemotherapy drug Navelbine, a newly discovered vinca alkaloid. Vinca—or periwinkle—is a genus of flowering plants. It contains at least eighty-six different alkaloids among the class of compounds with plant origins, which have pronounced physiological actions on humans. From the beginning of intake, apart from the usual side effects of loss of energy, loss of appetite, constipation, and sometimes diarrhea, Marina tolerated her new treatment pretty good. She was used to the mentioned symptoms long ago and treated them as an unavoidable evil. She was not tired of fighting, and her spirit was far from being conquered. Each time when I asked her how she felt, instead of a single word of complaint, her typical answer was something like, "Don't you worry, Vovka. It could be much worse."

Celebrating more than a decade of Marina's outstanding length of survival, her doctor and nurses honored Marina with the title "Our incredible patient." It may be hard to believe, but we at once perked up when Marina responded well to Navelbine. Ignoring active metastatic invasion in her body, we rekindled in our hearts a bright light of hope for the future. Marina tolerated Navelbine surprisingly well, and we hoped this would continue as long as possible. There was another good news at that time. One wonderful day, the hot flashes that had been seriously spoiling Marina's life for not less than thirty previous years suddenly disappeared. Lastly it came long expected time when she stopped having night sweats and the creeping feeling of intense warmth over her whole face and body. With the good response to Navelbine and the disappearance of her hot flashes, Marina's mood significantly improved. Her feelings of concern, worry, and anxiety calmed down to such a degree that one day when we were driving home from a grocery store, to my unspeakable amazement, unexpectedly, Marina took me back in time by resuming her baby-like talk. As in our golden times, we had a funny, delightful conversation between imaginary Piglet and Pooh. The short episodes of spontaneous baby-like talk occurred only two more times and then never repeated. Everything comes to an end.

Influenza Flu Type A

The day after the episode of baby talk, Marina was surprisingly silent and thoughtful. She didn't want to bother me with her problems, so when I asked her what was bothering her, she gave me a vague and short answer. When evening came, she told me that she had a fever; she drank little water and had hardly eaten since morning. It was clear that her condition was quickly deteriorating. I knew from earlier experience that Marina was rapidly losing fluid. She was prone to rapid dehydration, which usually necessitated hospitalization for treatment. Typically, intravenous infusion was effective in replenishing her fluids and normalizing metabolic processes. I have had countless opportunities to see that the introduction of intravenous fluid replacement into everyday medical practice as early as 1902 was one of the major advances in medicine and saved countless lives.

Marina struggled to drink liquids, but eventually she reached the point where, despite her best efforts, she could not drink at all. I knew from earlier experience that when she had difficulty swallowing liquids, she would soon become critically dehydrated.

Indeed, late in the evening of the same day, her condition worsened even more, and after some persuasion, she agreed that it was time to go to the emergency room. I was ready to take her by car, but her condition was so severe that she could not sit, so I called for paramedics. Only in America: five minutes after I hung up, paramedics, police, and fire truck drove up to us. While firefighters and police waited outside, two paramedics with a folding stretcher and boxes of medical supplies quickly entered the house and went up to the second floor, where Marina was. Both paramedics were professional and friendly. They instantly understood what was happening to Marina, who to that time could no longer speak. The important thing was that they agreed to take her to the hospital where her doctor worked. Wasting no time, they unfolded the stretcher and carefully laid Marina on it. Standing at the top of the stairs, I watched her being carried up the narrow stairs. When they were halfway down the stairs, I suddenly saw that Marina became completely motionless, and her face became pale as white paper. If

I had a clear mind and if she were not my wife, I would understand that she had passed out. But panic seized me, and I decided that she was dead or dying. Overwhelmed by panic, I shouted loudly again and again, "Marina," "Marina." The paramedics with the stretcher did not stop, but periodically glanced in my direction with sympathy. I'm sure my reaction was nothing new to them. When I went outside, Marina was already in the ambulance. When I came to the back door of the car, she opened her eyes and, to my infinite relief, nodded her bald head in my direction.

Once again, one of the paramedics assured me that Marina was being taken to the local hospital, where her doctor was. I thanked him and headed for the garage when the fire commander stood in my way. Because of the panic attack he witnessed, he was cautious, promising me that everything would be fine, but ordered me not to follow the ambulance on my car. I assured him that I was in complete control of my mind and had no intention of following the ambulance. However, this did not convince him, and he was ordering me again and again "not to go for the ambulance in my car." Avoiding protest, I patiently waited until, finally, having exhausted his warning, he left me.

By the time I arrived at the hospital, Marina had already been placed in one of the rooms of the ER. Intravenous fluids were started in the ambulance, so her condition improved slightly in a short time. She was weak, but conscious and alert. When she saw me, she asked me to bring her a couple of warm blankets and something to drink. When I returned, there was a nurse in the room who measured Marina's vital signs and took her blood for various tests. At that moment, the fear for Marina's life left me, and a wave of reassuring hope swept over me that everything would be okay.

Sitting next to Marina, as best I could, I reassured her that she would soon feel better. Before I left the practice, I worked in this hospital, and in the same emergency department, I was examining and admitting many patients in the past. I knew almost everyone around me, and they knew me, which made me feel comfortable and confident.

A chest X-ray was taken, after which an emergency doctor arrived, whom I had never met before. Obviously, he was new to this hospital. The clothes under his doctor's coat hinted that he was doing some construction work before going to work. He was wearing protective industrial boots, and there were traces of mud on his feet. Having greeted Marina blandly and demonstratively ignoring me, he proceeded to examine her. His examination was minimal. Like most doctors we know, he relied more on upcoming chest X-rays and blood tests than on the results of his own examination. The doctor spoke with a distinctive Russian accent, and although I tried to engage him in a conversation in our common language, he in no uncertain terms let me know that he did not like it. Finishing the preliminary assessment of Marina, he, to my surprise, expressed his satisfaction with his clinical impression, concluding it with a short phrase: "The patient's condition has improved." He left the room, promising to return when the X-ray and blood test results were ready. Knowing well Marina's state of health, I had no doubt that she needed immediate hospitalization, but when I heard the confident tone with which the ER doctor spoke about Marina's alleged "improvement," I became worried, suspecting that he was preparing us to refuse Marina's hospitalization.

Meanwhile, breathing more frequently than usual, Marina fell asleep. It was ten o'clock in the evening when she was awakened by the ER physician who had come back. From his appearance, I understood that I had been right in my assumption.

"Okay, all the results are back, and I checked them, Mrs. Tsesis," he said in such a pseudo-friendly tone as usually say people who want to hide their real intentions. "I do not see anything alarming with you right now. I just checked with the admitting office and learned that this hospital is extremely busy today, and, unfortunately, there is no hospital bed available tonight. Your lab tests are within normal limits, though, I should admit, your hemoglobin level is low. However, because of your main condition and current infection and metastatic cancer, there is nothing unusual in this finding. As for the chest X-ray, I see a small pulmonary infiltrate, but it will be taken care of with a strong antibiotic I will prescribe to take at home . . ."

"Sorry, doctor, but no way you can send my wife home," I interrupted him, protesting his intentions. "I cannot take her home. My wife needs fluids and antibiotics in the hospital setting, period. Look at her. She's a wreck. Read the paramedics' report; before she got here, she fainted. You can see for yourself that her rate of breathing is rapid, additional proof that she has pneumonia. On X-ray films the infiltrate might appear to be small, but we know her main condition is much more serious than the size of her infiltrate. As you know, she suffers from cancer with locations, and without doubt, her resistance to infection is strongly compromised."

"Sir, I am a doctor, and I have my own clinical judgement. In my opinion, your wife can be safely treated at home," the doctor responded calmly and confidently, looking impassively at Marina, who lay with her eyes closed.

The ER doctor was ready to leave when, by a happy accident, or maybe by the will of destiny, Marina's primary physician, Dr. Sittam, unexpectedly walked in. At that late hour, he was here to examine his another patient in the ER. Yes, not so long ago most primary physicians, when it was necessary, came to the ER to examine their private patients before admitting them to the hospital. Now, in the era of patient management by hospitalists, this practice, which used to be routine in this country, gradually fades into oblivion. Our beloved local doctor, judging by the worried expressions on the faces of Marina and me, could not believe that the ambulance doctor refused to hospitalize Marina. Avoiding confrontation, he told the emergency doctor that, as a staff doctor, he would admit Marina on his own name.

Things are so simple when you deal with caring—or, rather, with normal people. I am sure that I would have been able to insist on Marina's admission to the hospital myself, but it would have cost me nerves, which at this time were already on edge. I thought then that blessed are patients who have an opportunity to have an advocate for their health at a critical time. In the issue of life and death, as a physician, I have seen countless times that a patient's life was saved thanks to the interference of someone who cared for them, whether it was a physician, family, or simply a friend. I was happy when in less than an hour, Marina was transferred to a hospital room, where she continued to receive IV fluids, antibiotics, and other relatively simple but lifesaving measures started in the ER.

I went home late that night and returned early in the morning while Marina was still asleep. It was obvious she had not improved. To my disappointment, she still was pale, and her respiratory rate was frequent. I comforted myself with the thought that after all, I should not expect much after a short time of treatment. A lab tech came in and woke Marina to take blood tests. When the tech left, my wife gave me a weak smile and told me that she had slept better than on the previous night. Our conversation was interrupted by the arrival of two X-ray technicians who deftly rolled an X-ray unit into the room. Taking films at Marina's bedside, they left as quickly as they'd arrived.

Dr. Sittam soon entered the room. Knowledgeable, experienced, friendly, and caring, he began his rounds early in the morning. To be examined during early morning rounds is a great favor for patients, who need to know what will be their disposition that day.

After finishing examining Marina, Dr. Sittam informed us about the results of her recent diagnostic tests. Since the X-rays revealed the progression of the pneumonia against the background of signs of active inflammation and a decreased blood hemoglobin level, Dr. Sittam not only ordered stronger antibiotics for Marina, but also, based on her previous favorable experience, he planned to give her blood transfusion.

Marina's recovery was slow, but her body once again proved its strength and perseverance. Her condition stabilized. Being a woman of action who never forgot to take care of her health, she asked Dr. Sittam if she should continue her current chemotherapy regimen while she was in the hospital. He promised to get in touch with her oncologist to discuss the issue.

Early in the evening of the same day, Dr. Sittam came in for his second clinical round. He told Marina that Dr. Miller had told him that her chemo could be safely stopped for the next ten days.

"Are you sure it will not make my health worse?" Marina asked with anxiety in her voice.

"Don't worry, Marina," Doctor Sittam reassured her tenderly. "Your oncologist told me straight and clear that it will not affect your prognosis at all. So don't you worry."

Marina did not hide her relief. These days there is an overabundance of educational materials available about different oncological conditions. However, what is lacking is an availability of explanation of the universal strategic principles that govern course and treatment of oncological condition. Probably in order to not commit themselves to their predictions, oncological specialists are overwhelmingly reluctant to discuss openly the anticipated milestones of the illness. What is a simple knowledge to an oncologist often is unknown to a patient. Patients who face dramatic changes in the course of their illness need to have the proper knowledge about what they could expect in the near and far future. Usually, patients are not hiding from the truth, and they would substantially benefit if they would be introduced to the general principles of their particular condition. Marina's question about temporary discontinuation of chemo was in this category.

Though on the third day of Marina's hospitalization, her general condition continued to gradually improve, her temperature remained elevated, and her appetite was practically absent. My main occupation at this time was to keep offering her all kinds of foods. Frequent attempts to give her Ensure and other nutritional drinks continued to be counterproductive. Finally, after many trial-and-error attempts, we discovered what Marina tolerated and that she also liked the sourdough bread, cheddar-broccoli soup from a local Panera restaurant, and Dove chocolate ice cream.

On the fourth day of hospitalization, Marina received a blood transfusion. Once again, I was impressed with the great healing results of that procedure. Several hours after it was over, Marina's hemoglobin, which before had been 8.0 g/dl, was slightly above 9 g/dl. Her skin changed from pale to almost normal flesh color. The transfusion gave her renewed energy, and when I got back to her room, she was immersed in her favorite pastime—reading a book.

Marina was discharged on her sixth day in the hospital. Before she was discharged, Dr. Sittam came in with an expression on his face that said he had important news. Coming close to Marina, who was in the bed, he handed her a piece of paper.

"Look, what you went through, Marina," he said, trying not to be dramatic. "You suffered from no less a disease than influenza type A. Even healthy people often die from this infection, and you managed to successfully beat it. That means you are a strong person, Marina Tsesis. Yes, if you were able to triumph over such an aggressive virus with all your other problems, you will surely live to be one hundred and twenty. You are a great soldier."

Marina was soon discharged and supplied with prescriptions for oral antibiotics and medications for her symptoms.

Discussing Past Events

On the fifth day after her discharge, Marina visited Dr. Miller, who asked her many questions about the course of the viral infection. Like Dr. Sittam, she was impressed that although Marina's immunity was compromised by her cancer, she had been able to successfully recover without any complications from a serious viral disease. When Dr. Miller finished congratulating her on her stamina, Marina smiled sadly and reminded the doctor about the episode in 2013 when she was responding poorly to Abraxane, and when her earlier oncologist had strongly recommended her to stop cancer treatment and to be transferred to hospice care.

"I highly respected and trusted the clinical opinion of my previous oncologist," Marina said. "However, I still cannot believe how she would simply write me out of life without afterwards apology. It is hard to believe but if I had followed her advice, I would have been dead long time ago. How can one explain her outrageous decision, and how could such a highly acclaimed physician be so irresponsible? I hope I was the first and the last person she subjected to such a cruel decision. At the same time, I wonder what might have happened to a patient with less access to medical knowledge than I am privileged to have. How can you justify the death sentence she handed to me?"

Though Marina knew well that for ethical and legal reasons, Dr. Miller could not express her true opinion, the answer of her present doctor was meaningful enough.

"I really do not know why she said so," Dr. Miller said while reviewing Dr. Arnold's original notes on the computer. "It is difficult for me to comment on such an inflammatory issue. The only thing I can say is that besides Abraxane, which you did not tolerate back then, there were chemo agents that could have been tried. I don't know why she did not offer them to you."

For the umpteenth time, I realized that often our destiny depends on nothing but a lucky chance. After Dr. Arnold had unequivocally and cruelly determined Marina's place in the hospice, if not for common efforts of relatives and friends, she would have been in heaven long ago. Everything that has happened since then has no doubt confirmed how wrong she was. Isn't it a medical mistake when seriously ill people cannot get the right advice, thus becoming a victim of a raw medical arbitrariness? Usually this happens because chronically busy doctors make sometimes too-hasty conclusions and forget that an integral part of their profession is a respect for human life. After Dr. Arnold in 2013 unambiguously told that Marina's place was in the hospice, if not for Marina's resolve and the availability of family and friends who were physicians, she would have died long ago. What happened after 2013's fatal conversation unequivocally confirmed how deadly wrong Dr. Arnold had been when she was stealing years of her patient's life. It is a real tragedy when seriously ill people do not have access to proper advice and meekly allow themselves to become victims of an unchecked doctor's authority. Along with the tremendous help provided by many doctors, some of them are being too rushed or impatient to think properly, forgetting the honorary mission of their profession.

FoundationOne CDx Study

News of the introduction of new methods of treatment serves as a great help in raising the spirits of cancer patients. Similar positive developments supply a fuel that helps maintain the flames of hope in their souls. In January 2017 when Marina received Navelbine treatment, we learned about one of such promising news. Dr. Miller told us that she wanted Marina to take part in recently becoming popular new FoundationOne CDx study, which was clinically and analytically confirmed for all solid tumors.

Sophisticated FoundationOne CDx testing uses comprehensive genomic profiling (CGP) by searching 324 genes for cancer-relevant mutations in the DNA of the patient's tumor cells. The results of the test are supposed to help the doctor to explore treatment options. Most importantly, based on the specific, unique genetic type of a particular patient's cancer, FoundationOne CDx testing individualizes treatment of patients by setting up what medication or combination of medications could be most optimal.

In a couple of weeks, Marina's test results came back. Dr. Miller told us she was pleased with the result. Although FoundationOne CDx testing rarely gives precise recommendations, in Marina's case, the recommendation was certain. It found that the ideal combination for treatment of Marina's cancerous process besides Navelbine, which she was already taking, would be the added drug Tamoxifen. Tamoxifen, an estrogen antagonist, is a popular synthetic drug used to treat breast cancer and infertility in women. Dr. Miller put a lot of hope in the received recommendation and at once added Tamoxifen to Marina's therapeutic regimen.

Marina's relatively good condition, along with the new approach to treatment, could not help but cheer us up once again. After our earlier challenges, our imagined *Hope* life's ship set sail again and entered the quiet waters of normal life. For the umpteenth time, we conveniently forgot that Marina's life was wedged between a rock and a hard place. Like countless people before and after us that we met in the world of oncology, when we felt good and were without pain, we continued to behave as though life would never end. Is there any other choice? Whatever happens, life goes on. Whether or not we want to admit it, we are mortal beings, which does not prevent us from enjoying our lives as long as our physical and mental health allows it.

New Venous Access Port

One of the complications during Marina's recent hospitalization was a discovery that her veins, though they were easily visible, once again became difficult to access for IVs, drawing blood, and imaging studies. Just as during her initial chemotherapy in 2005, the wide caliber of needles had quickly put her veins out of service. After several unpleasant experiences with starting IV lines, Marina remembered the beneficial experience with venous access port in 2005 and asked Dr. Miller for placement of a port. The placement was performed by a surgeon, and in the future, until the last days of her life, it helped her with inconveniences of unsuccessful phlebotomies. While the port's maintenance is minimal, nurses who use this device for intravenous injection require a special certification.

Metastases Became Highly Resistant to Treatment

Unfortunately, Navelbine and Tamoxifen combination recommended by FoundationOne CDx genetic study was effective for less than half a year. In reality, everything in our lives is relative, and half a year for a patient with multiple metastases could be considered a long period of time. In February 2017, Dr. Miller informed Marina that in reviewing her regularly taken CT and body scan, she noticed further progression of liver's and, to a lesser extent, lungs' metastases. Though she expressed this news without noticeable signs of alarm, her statement awakened in me a familiar and strong sense of anxiety.

"With these changes, should we worry? Is it something serious?" I asked the oncologist anxiously. Marina, who consistently focused her attention only on immediate events, would never ask this type of question. Dr. Miller's ever-present encouraging smile disappeared from her lips for a moment. With a serious expression, she looked first at Marina and then at me and gave us a firm answer. "I do not think so. I promise that if such a situation ever arises, I will let you know."

Because I was always trying to see positive in the current events, her words placated me for a long time. As for Marina, my dearest natural philosopher did not show visible signs of concern or worry. The main thing for her was that during this particular period of time, she was active and independent.

Another Genetic Study

In another decisive attempt to decide what drug to give Marina on a scientific basis, Dr. Miller ordered for Marina a new round of genetic research. Two weeks later, when we came for a follow-up examination, according to the result of this study, Dr. Miller opted for a new method of treatment. This time it was a combination of two drugs: Arimidex, which Marina took in 2005, and Afinitor.

Afinitor (everolimus) is a cancer medicine that interferes with the growth of cancer cells and slows their spread in the body. Used with other types of cancer, it is used for breast cancer as well. Though it has many side effects, my resilient wife did not experience them. Among other chemo medications, even with Medicare and Supplemental Insurance, Afinitor was an expensive drug for the patient. A co-pay for a monthly supply was a significant amount of money, but who cares about money when human life is at stake!

Afinitor is an inhibitor of kinase, a type of protein in the body. Kinases help all cells, both healthy and cancerous, to get the energy they need. When kinases do not act normally or are overactive, they help certain breast cancers grow. Kinase inhibitors work by stopping the cancer cells from getting the energy they need to grow.

Initially, Afinitor in combination with Arimidex produced a beneficial effect on Marina's health, without any of the potentially bad side effects. After numerous chemotherapy courses, she returned to her normal health, and for a while, nothing prevented us from enjoying each other's company as in good old time. Though she had stopped going to the fitness club and we'd both stopped traveling a good while ago, we continued to visit our friends, went to concerts, and watched TV and videos. Marina's physical health was not as strong as before, but she was not only able to take care of herself, but she continued to be in charge of the household duties and performed almost all of them with a minimal help from me, never complaining but enjoying her work. She never stopped to believe that being active helped her to forget about the problems with her health. She also kept up her study of Hebrew as well as actively took part in the lives of the family members, attended religious services, and most of all, she continued to enjoy reading. In the evening before falling asleep, she read in bed, and to avoid the weight of thick books and to benefit from a larger font, she began to use a Kindle device. Gradually, the Kindle device became her only tool for reading needs. She carried it with her wherever she went.

Skin Metastases

One evening I entered into Marina's room and found her carefully examining the skin below her breasts' area. When I approached her, she showed me a raised rash consisting of several scattered pinkish lesions. Without any sign of ulceration and with a smooth surface, the rash appeared benign and did not portend any threat. Marina told me that she had noticed the changes three months ago, but she did not want to bother me with it since they had been much less pronounced then.

A week later, when Dr. Miller examined the rash, she said nothing about her impression and just advised Marina to continue to keep an eye on the lesions. She told her that even if her skin changes were of a metastatic nature, the chemotherapy she was presently receiving should take care of the problem and that there was a good possibility the lesions would disappear soon.

Dr. Miller was right. In six or seven weeks, Marina's skin lesions shrank significantly in size. Marina and I were happy that the Afinitor and Arimidex combination had helped the skin metastases disappear and hoped the treatment would also have a good chance to affect her other metastases.

Restored Vision

Facing enormous challenges, Marina, with her attitude toward life, continued to retain her natural ability to feel happy and find reasons to enjoy life. Unfortunately, at that time, she developed difficulty with her vision. Since she was an avid reader, this presented for her a serious problem. When an ophthalmologist diagnosed her with bilateral cataracts and offered to surgically remove them, Marina did not hesitate to schedule the surgery right away. For her, normal life was unthinkable without her ability to enjoy books--her major refuge from all of life's troubles. Not giving much thought to her main problem, Marina focused all her attention on preparing for the cataract surgery. The two surgeries, one for each eye, were scheduled with an interval of two weeks, and the cataracts were removed without incident. After her normal vision returned, Marina excitedly shared her joy about the results of the surgery with her friends.

Marina achieved a perfection in her ability to compartmentalize perception of the daily reality. "I am so happy that I had the surgery," she would tell them. "It is so wonderful to be able to read books and work on the computer without my eyes getting tired. Most exciting is that before the surgery, the world appeared to me with yellowish hue, cloudy, and with a halo. I thought that at my age, this is how it should be, but now the world around me appears crisp and clear, without a yellow hue. I did not ever imagine having such a terrific result. Now the world appears to me just as I saw it when I was young."

While Hair Comes and Goes, the Beauty Remains

I never knew that the amount of a cancer patient's hair loss depends on which specific chemo drug is used. During her long years of treatment, Marina lost her hair several times, sometimes completely and sometimes partially, and then to some degree, she grew it back.

Once in a while, her lost hair grew back on her head as if out of nowhere. During these times, hair reappeared not only on Marina's head, but newly grown eyebrows and eyelashes adorned her beautiful face again. Corresponding to her age, her head hair was now gray, but her new grown eyebrows and eyelashes were always moderately dark. Regrettably, the times when she was bald could last for years, so during this period of time, she wore different headcovers such as a cloche hat, slouch hat, or a turban.

When she began to take Afinitor, we had a big surprise. I believed when hair turned gray, it could never regain its former color, but I was wrong. A couple of months after she took Afinitor, she not only got a good part of her hair back, but suddenly and to Marina's joy, instead of being gray, at least half of her new hair was dark, which pleasantly added to her appearance. She hated covering her head and was happy to have her own hair back.

While Marina was not emotionally involved with her deteriorating medical condition, she continued to pay a lot of attention to her appearance that indisputably was affected by the illness. The main person she wanted to please was she, herself. To retain beauty and attractiveness in her own eyes, she spent considerable time on the internet, searching for nice clothing. She was not very fond of wearing jewelry, so I had to use all kinds of excuses, such as birthdays and anniversaries dates, to persuade her to make additions to her jewelry collection.

Looking at my Marina, a seventy-three-year-old woman, whose body was ravaged with years of severe health problems, as strange as it might sound, in my eyes, she still appeared beautiful, attractive, and charming, as if she was fifty-two years ago when we met first on the sandy beach of the Black Sea. Somehow, my eyes and my mind did a trick, and before me was Marina's face, young and unchanged with age.

Her worsening condition now prevented her from volunteering at the school where our grandchildren studied, so to experience "the golden time," as she called it, she looked for other meaningful things to do with them, as well as she found ways to possibly contribute to the world despite her health.

Holocaust Materials

For many years our son, Alexander, had been interested in the tragic issues of the Holocaust. As a professor at a university, he received numerous unique educational materials about German atrocities committed in the occupied territories of the Soviet Union during World War II from a curator of one of the Holocaust Memorial Museums. His goal was to write a book about German fascist crimes against humanity, based on primary sources from the

Soviet Union. Most of this material consisted of documented records of the interrogations of individuals who had witnessed Hitler's barbarisms with their own eyes.

Marina had previously worked with similar documents, for which she had been recognized by researchers at that same museum. When she learned of our son's project in 2015, she had volunteered to help him with the classification and organization of the materials he received. Ever since, she had worked with the documents for two or more hours a day, often discussing different issues with our son on the phone. She stopped this research just two months before she left this world, when her deteriorating health did not allow her to be active.

Spiritual Values

Early morning prayer services, which we continued to attend, required Marina's strict discipline. The services started at 7:30 a.m., and to be on time at the temple, Marina now needed more time to get ready for the service than when she had been healthier and stronger.

While Marina believed in God, I do not remember that she ever started a conversation about the subject of God. She listened to me attentively when I spoke to her about different theological issues, from time to time, offering her own comments. Religion for her was an intimate and lofty subject that she hardly ever volunteered to discuss with anybody, me included. We continued to attend a religious service every morning, we observed Shabbat, we observed High Holidays, and overall, we led a traditionally Jewish, though very far from Orthodox, way of life. I used to read books on theology, but Marina followed religious precepts the way her ancestors did. It can be said that she was a religious woman who accepted religion in her heart, while theology was absolutely not "her cup of tea."

When Marina had a year and a half left to live, I had an unexpected and surprising opportunity to see the tangible confirmation of Marina's deep inner, intuitive approach to religion.

For the last couple of years, various medical reasons had compelled us to sleep in separate rooms on the second floor, our bedroom doors opened onto the corridor. Most of the time, Marina kept her bedroom's door open, but sometimes she would close it. Appreciating her privacy, I never walked into her room without knocking. One evening when her door was ajar, I saw Marina deeply concentrated on her thoughts, standing silently in front of the open door to her walk-in closet. I did not have any idea what was going on until a couple of months later when--again passing the open door of her room--I saw Marina in the same pose as I saw her the earlier time. Dressed in her home bathrobe, she stood silently before the walk-in closet door, her eyes closed and her lips slightly moving. It dawned on me that my wife was praying on her own. Not wanting to disturb her in her spiritual experience, I carefully closed the door and went about my business.

Witnessing the same picture several more times, finally unable to resist, carefully so as not to hurt her feelings, once I confessed her what I had un-wittingly saw and asked her to confirm that what I'd unintentionally seen was her personal prayers to God. Having lived together for fifty-five happy years and trusting each other unconditionally, we hardly ever kept secrets from each other. However, in the ensuing loud silence, I understood what she did not want to confess to me. Looking at her, without her saying a word, I understood, that her prayers had been for her deep personal meaning, and that she felt that sharing the sacred words of her personal prayers might trivi-alize its sincere and pure content.

Weeks later, not appreciating the earlier lesson enough, I dared to ask Marina again what she had been praying for. This time she gave me such a long, reproachful look that since then I never asked her this question again.

Love Is Like a Dream

As Marina's disease progressed further, her expression of love for me, an eternal love that shone like a lighthouse all through the previous years of our lives together, was still there, but now it was expressed in a different way from during previous years. Before, her love had been confirmed by the loving looks she sent me, by her friendly and enticing smiles, or by a spontaneous kiss and light touch when I passed by. But now she became much more reserved in showing her feelings. The greatest proof that I was still her beloved now was not direct demonstrations of it, but it could be revealed when I overheard her talking with our friends, either in person or on the phone. During these conversations, I heard phrases like "My Vovka told me . . .," "My Vovka thinks that this will be right . . .," or "My Vovka mentioned this . . ." Her affectionate words told me that I continued to occupy a special place in her mind and heart and that she loved me as much as she did in the past.

It was only normal that after many years of a challenging and devastating disease with its countless ups and downs, Marina became more and more focused on herself. Being actively involved in the treatment of her disease and managing one tough symptom after another, her mind was now focused on her survival. Nevertheless, as usual, not a single word of complaint came from her lips, and her eyes still lit up brightly at the sight of our grandchildren.

Never complaining, Marina periodically betrayed what truly was on her mind when I asked her how she really felt. First, she would say quietly that she was doing well, and then spontaneously, as an afterthought, as if she were speaking to herself, she would add in a low voice something like "I live now for you and for our children."

Gradually, more and more she moved away from having the worldview of a healthy person. Now her main concern was how to function despite her debilitating condition. The ongoing encroachment by cancer metastases made her stop working with our son on his Holocaust project. At the same time, she still did not give up performing small chores at home by herself. She still liked to shop, but now I accompanied her when she went to the grocery or department store.

The Stomach as the Mirror of the Soul

Pressures related to Marina's health influenced my own well-being. My stomach was affected the most. The heartburn that had bothered me since adolescence now became severe, and taming it required me to take daily proton pump inhibitors—medications that reduce stomach acid production—plus a handful of antacids. Even though seriously ill herself, Marina never stopped being sensitive to my needs. She remained my guardian angel, albeit now she was my slow-moving guardian angel, and whenever I had an appointment with my doctor, she insisted on accompanying me there.

Never Stopping the Hourglass of Time

As the cancer did its vicious job, Marina did not stop taking care of her appearance. But in addition to her preoccupation with her own nice clothing, she started paying attention to my clothing as well. Initially, I could not understand why unexpectedly I had so many new shirts, pants, and suits in my closet. Once, when I objected, not answering and staring at me, she listened silently to my protests. Finally, it dawned on me what was written in her eyes. I was not smart enough to understand by myself that never forgetting to care for those for whom she felt responsible, she was preparing me for the time when she would not be around me and when I will be left without her help.

Meanwhile, though Marina was refusing to look into the future, she could not escape the merciless blows of her own illness. It was obvious that the gravity of cancer was beginning to take its hard toll on her. On two occasions, while we were involved in intimate conversation and our souls seemed to merge with each other, she looked deep into my eyes and muttered in a sad voice, "Poor, Vovka, it will be very difficult for you to be without me."

"Stop predicting things that are not predictable, Marina," I objected, trying to be cheerful. "Do not forget that twenty years ago I had quintuple-bypass heart surgery, so you might as well become a widow, though with God's help, we will die together on the same day."

My Dulcinea, my Juliet, my Iseult, my Galatea in one image did not comment on my objection. She only closed her tired eyelids and murmured, as if to herself, "Poor, Vovka; poor, Vovka."

I objected to her concerns as I could and again and again asked her to not have dark thoughts and continue to fight, to fight, and to fight. She never disagreed; she just looked at me and said nothing. Even without her saying it, I knew well she would not stop to fight, not so much for herself as for all those whom she loved and to whom she was devoted.

Trying to do the same that I asked Marina to do, I did my best to silence my dark thoughts about the future. In our trustworthy boat of hope, which was isolated from hurricanes and storms, we continued to sail on the wide river of life.

However, the fate has its own way. Marina was gradually leaving the world of sounds and images; her energy level decreased day by day and the many household chores she still insisted on doing took her much longer time to perform. Still trying to be independent, she categorically refused my help whenever she could. As weak, thin, and fragile as she was, she continued to take daily showers without help. To avoid prolonged standing during this occupation, she used a special stool placed in the bathtub.

She had already stopped walking outside and now spent almost all her time at home. When we went to the grocery store, while she slowly pushed the shopping cart, I ran from aisle to aisle with the shopping list and then returned to her, gradually filling the cart with groceries.

Over the years of meeting countless victims of life-threatening conditions, their courage and their ability to keep their dignity never failed to deeply impress me. Facing serious challenges, the full severity of which is known only to them, they live with their chins held high. Staring down the face of departure from this world of countless wonders, these people have the courage to act—to paraphrase a popular song—as if they are going to live forever and will never die. All victims of a terminal illness deserve words of praise and admiration. Until her last breath, Marina never lost hope, believing her suffering was not in vain.

Celebrating the Longevity Record

On New Year's Eve 2018, the last new year of Marina's life, we celebrated with members of our close family. Among the toasts given were many for Marina's health. By this time, she'd achieved almost thirteen years of survival with advanced metastatic cancer. Actually, considering that when she was diagnosed, the tumor was already at least two years old, her survival was really fifteen years. Without a doubt, if she were not so responsible and courageous in taking care of her health, she would never have endured all those long years. On this New Year's Eve, she said an emotional toast for our children and grandchildren. Afterward we took a family photo, where my wife's smile on the picture looked healthy and full of life.

Traveling Together

Marina had been behind the steering wheel when we drove to the New Year's party, but when the party was over and we were on our way home, she was so tired that she asked me to do the driving. For many years in the past, like many backseat drivers, Marina was "generous" with comments about what she considered lapses in my driving. I knew she was just trying to help me, but at the same time, I thought it was unnecessary, and sometimes even dangerous, to give me advice for situations that did not require her interference. I hardly ever argued with her, not only because I loved her but also because I did not like to waste precious time of our life on petty arguments. The most I would do would be to offer to change places so she could drive instead of me. She would refuse to take me up on the offer but continued to make comments about my driving.

One day I thought I found the proper argument in my wish to stop Marina's unnecessary participation in my driving. I delicately told her that her comments might be counterproductive because for forty years of driving, I had not had a single accident. "When you drive the car," I told her, "we talk, I read you a book, we listen to radio, and I never criticize your driving. Just trust me with your life as I trust you, please."

Other arguments that I've used in the past were unsuccessful, but to my surprise, this time I was so persuasive that once and for all, Marina stopped being a backseat driver. Her hands-off attitude helped our car travel to be more secure and relaxed for both of us.

Yet, while driving this New Year's night, for some reason, Marina couldn't take her eyes off the road.

"What's going on?" I finally asked her. "Is something wrong?"

"Yes, there is," she answered. "I know I should not interfere with your driving, but don't you think you are driving too far away to the left in your lane? Isn't that dangerous?"

I carefully checked the car's position in the lane and did not find anything wrong with it.

"No, Marina. There is nothing wrong in the car's position in the lane, I assure you," I answered. "Could it be that your recent cataract surgery is responsible for an optical illusion?"

"Okay, I believe you," Marina said. "But I still do not understand why I clearly see that you are driving too far away to the left in your lane."

I was wrong in blaming Marina's New Year's problem with vision on the cataract surgery. I was to learn the real cause for that night's optical illusion only several months later.

Gradual Hearing Loss

Starting from the middle of 2017, Marina met another problem. This time it was gradually increasing hearing loss. Approximately one in three people between the ages of sixty-five and seventy-four has hearing loss, so I explained for myself Marina's hearing loss was related to her age and not for a minute I suspected that I was wrong. Neither I paid much attention that her hearing loss was not accompanied with such typical symptom for otosclerosis as difficulty hearing low-pitched sounds or whispers, and that she did not hear ringing or hissing in her ears known as tinnitus. As Marina's problem was progressing, eventually she went to visit the ear, nose, and throat specialist. The specialist, not finding typical symptoms for otosclerosis, referred her to an audiologist. The audiologist, a pleasant, middle-aged woman, confirmed that Marina had hearing loss of unknown nature and recommended a hearing aid. Several following visits were dedicated to adjusting this expensive device to Marina's individual needs. If while visiting the oncologist, we often were destined to receive unpleasant news, our visits to the audiologist--for a change--were an enjoyable experience. Marina, a sociable person, was happy to have a hearing aid and did not part with it day and night.

Similar to Marina's previously mentioned optical illusion when she thought I had problem with driving, I didn't expect to get a dramatic explanation of her vision and hearing problems soon.

Back Pain and Prolonged Adventure with Morphine

In June 2018, Marina's condition markedly worsened. One morning with this background, Marina woke up with a severe back pain. As it happened before, it was impossible to establish the origin of this particular episode of pain. Over-the-counter painkillers were not effective. Her pain was so sharp that she contacted the oncologist by phone, who recommended her to go straight to the hospital for direct admission. We gathered all the necessary things and headed to our garage. My heart sank when I saw how Marina with a determined expression on her face, with a hesitant gait, stooped and slowly walked toward the car. It was still early morning, and the roads were not busy yet, so soon we were in the hospital's admission office. After signing the documents in the admission office, a woman transporter took Marina to the hospital floor.

Her private room was shining with cleanliness, technological advancements, and comfort. For me was available a comfortable armchair, and a smartly designed folding bed.

Within a short time, first a nurse, then a medical student, then a resident examined Marina. The last to arrive was the hospitalist on call. This doctor had a pleasant bedside manner and appeared to be knowledgeable. He told us that in addition to other diagnostic tests, in the morning, Marina will have an MRI to discern the possible reason for her excruciating backache. Marina told him that the strong painkillers she was taking before admission did not help her, and the hospitalist decided that her condition justified use of morphine. He explained to her that because various people need different doses, following special hospital protocol, he would start her with the possibly lowest and hopefully effective dose of morphine. If that dose was not effective, he would gradually increase it until the optimal level was achieved. Before leaving Marina, the hospitalist on call let her know that tomorrow, during morning rounds, she would be examined by her attending physician who had a lot of experience with morphine use. Shortly after the hospitalist left, a nurse delivered into the room IV unit intended for infusion of morphine.

Before the drug overdose epidemic began in our country, morphine was given in such a liberal manner that with the help of a button, the patients could easily increase the dose until their pain was under control. However, due to bureaucratic national regulations enacted with the best intentions to prevent possible addiction to morphine, that simple and highly effective method was drastically changed. According to the revised policy, the patient could still regulate the dosage, but only within a strictly limited range. For example, when the patient reached the maximum ordered dosage and it did not bring relief from the pain, the patient was supposed to call the nurse and ask her to increase the dose. According to regulations, the nurse was supposed to request the doctor on call to increase the dose, which the doctor will endorse, but not more than by 10 percent.

After an hour of infusion, Marina didn't feel that her pain was decreasing. The nurse, to whom she complained, promised to get in touch with the doctor on duty. Obviously, the doctor authorized the increase, because the nurse reappeared in the room right away and pushed buttons on the IV pump to increase the dose. The enhanced dose did not reduce Marina's pain but remembering that I had not eaten since the morning, she ordered me to go to the hospital cafeteria. Expecting that during the time I will spend in the cafeteria, her pain will subside, I deliberately spent more time in the cafeteria than it was necessary. Alas, my hope of finding Marina relieved from pain did not come through. There was a slight improvement in the intensity of the pain in her lumbar area, but in the rest of her spine, the pain remained excruciating, preventing her from resting. I suggested to ask the nurse to call the doctor again to request increase of the morphine's dose, but Marina declined. Expecting the medication to start working, she wanted to wait with a call to the doctor. Another four hours passed, but the pain did not diminish, so, disappointed, she called the nurse to increase the morphine dose. Unfortunately, it appeared that the shift nurse did not like to be bothered repeatedly for the same reason. "Let me call the physician and discuss your request. We will see what he says," she told Marina dryly in an officious tone.

More than an hour and a half passed until she returned and told Marina that she'd gotten in touch with the doctor on call, who endorsed her request to increase the dose of morphine by another 10 percent.

Alas, once again the increased dose did not have the desired effect. Two hours passed, but Marina's excruciating pain did not subside. It persisted the entire night, and she waited impatiently for the morning rounds so she could ask the attending physician to finally give her the proper dose to help alleviate her suffering.

In the morning, a large group of medics entered the room, including Marina's attending physician, a fellow, two residents, two medical students, and a hospital pharmacist. Not waiting for the attending physician to ask her questions, Marina said to him he must help her. She told him emphatically that she had been in great pain all night and that it was cruel. Then she added that she hardly slept the entire previous night because the doses of morphine given to her weren't effective for her. "I will never get rid of the pain if you continue to increase the morphine dose so slowly," she concluded.

The doctor, who listened to Marina attentively, assured her that he would do his best to help her. "You have to understand that we are between a rock and a hard place," addressing not only Marina but the others in the room, he said. "On one hand we want to control the pain, and on the other, we do not want the dose to be too high and thus be responsible for the patient's addiction to narcotics, especially when it comes to morphine. That's why according to the new recommendations, we increase the morphine's dose very gradually, only by 10 percent at a time."

"Doctor, for your information, I have never been given narcotics in my entire life. I am a conscientious person, I am seventy-five, and it is absurd to think that at my age and with my character, I would ever become a druggie.

Does not the fact that I have terminal cancer convince you that you can be more flexible in my case?"

The attending physician only nodded affirmatively, not honoring Marina with a worthy answer. And why should he answer such a patient? The doctor was on his territory. If a doctor or a nurse or even a nurse's aide labeled a patient as to be "too demanding," or synonymously as "hysterical"--and as an insider I know countless examples of it--they had many ways to prove the patient was "unreasonable." Compassion and empathy do not earn medics any more in wages. Insurance companies do not demand it and do not pay for it. Why bother? The doctor could easily explain his failure to answer a question by saying he was so struck by what the patient said to him that he became speechless. There is no doubt that the doctor would be much more sensitive to Marina's complaints if she were a member of his family, or if he, himself, had experienced the same pain as she did that night. Just because someone is a doctor does not mean at all that empathy with the suffering of a patient is a part of his or her character. At the same time, it must be said that the majority of physicians are doing their best to help their patients.

As if Marina's words meant nothing to him, the attending physician turned to his team and began discussing in an undertone the strategy of pain control with them. The main person he addressed was a hospital pharmacist, who, between taking notes and using sophisticated scientific jargon, explained what he recommended.

Since the group left the room, although Marina's morphine dose was increased twice, she was still suffering from pain. At 9:00 p.m., I needed to handle an urgent matter at home and was forced to leave her. Always attentive to my well-being, Marina asked me not to forget to call her when I arrived there. An hour later, I was at home. Remembering my wife's wish, the first thing I did was call her hospital room. Marina picked up the phone and answered. Initially she sounded quite rational, then suddenly, in the middle of conversation, she became confused, using words and phrases that lacked any logic. I did not doubt that, by sheer coincidence, exactly when I called, her blood's concentration of morphine surpassed the therapeutic level, which produced a deep somnolent effect on her. In another few minutes, her speech became completely gibberish, which ended in complete silence. Unable to believe in the irony how the overzealous management of the morphine had ended in an overdose, I repeated my calls to Marina over and over again, this time to her cell phone, but there was no answer. It was obvious that she had passed out from an overdose.

A high dose of morphine can suppress and eventually stop a person's breathing with an eventual fatal outcome. In my vivid imagination, I thought that there was a possibility the pharmacy had mistakenly delivered too high a dose of morphine. The other possibility was that she might have had a stroke. With my hands shaking, I called the nursing station and fortunately was able to get in touch with my wife's nurse right away. She listened to my concerns and promised to call me back after checking on Marina's condition. She kept her word and in ten minutes, she let me know that though Marina was in a deep sleep and her vital signs were normal, she did not respond to repeated attempts to wake her up. For this reason, she had called the doctor on duty, and he was on his way. The nurse promised to call me right away after the doctor examined my wife.

Worried that due to the morphine overdose Marina could stop breathing any moment, I was greatly relieved when I heard the phone ring. This time it was the physician on duty. He told me that "as hard as it was to believe," Marina had indeed experienced a morphine overdose. He ordered Naloxone for her, a morphine antidote, which--he assured me--should take care of the problem at once. After I expressed my deep worry about the possible effects of the overdose and the antidote, he told me that Marina's nurse would check on her every ten minutes and that she would call me back in half an hour to let me know about my wife's condition. I patiently waited for a call from the nurse, but more than three-quarters of an hour passed, and the phone stayed silent. Extremely nervous about how Marina had responded to the Naloxone injection, I called her cell phone in expectation that she had regained consciousness. Not receiving an answer, I called the nurse again. When she eventually picked up, she had no idea what was going on with her patient recently. She politely apologized and promised to call me back with a report right away. Alas, at least twenty minutes passed, but she still did not call me back.

Worried about what was going on, with a pounding heart, I ran out to the garage, started the car, and drove straight to the hospital. I was speeding and was lucky the police did not stop me. Reaching the hospital in record time and short of breath, I ran into Marina's room. Next to the door, there was standing a group of nurses signing off their shifts.

"Which one of you takes care of my wife in 7002?" I asked them before running into Marina's room.

A charming nurse with rosy cheeks and a friendly smile raised her hand.

"Dear nurse, you promised me to about my wife's condition, but you never called me back. Isn't that outrageous?" looking straight in her eyes, I said indignantly.

The nurse looked at me like she did not understand what I was trying to say. She shrugged as if I were a museum exhibit, then looked at her colleagues, silently asking for sympathy about what kind of public she has to deal with.

When I entered Marina's room, she was in a deep sleep. It took me a few minutes to awaken her. When she slowly opened her eyes, she recognized me and asked for a glass of water. After a couple of sips, she smiled faintly and greeted me in a low voice.

I breathed a sigh of relief, once again struck by the irony of what had happened. All that scientific, sophisticated control over the morphine dosage had achieved nothing but a drug overdose that could have led to respiratory arrest and even the death of a patient, especially when the patient was in the room alone and was not monitored. What could have happened if I had not called Marina just when the symptoms of her narcotic overdose had begun?

The next day, still upset about nurse's lack of responsibility in monitoring the patient and failing to keep me posted about the episode, I complained to the floor's head nurse. She nodded her head when I finished and promised to investigate my complaint. However, judging by her tone, I understood that she did not take my grievance seriously. After years of working as a physician, I should have known that complaining about a nurse to the floor's head nurse was mostly a useless exercise because, as in my case, it would be my word against the nurse's word. The hospital's nurse services are independent and are under the direct control of the hospital's head nurse, whose first priority is keeping a good reputation of her department and to be in good relationship with the administration and the public at large.

After Marina received injection of Naloxone to counteract the morphine overdose, the doctor on duty temporarily canceled her morphine. Surprisingly, this discontinuation of morphine coincided with a marked reduction in the intensity of Marina's back pain. Such paradoxical things are nothing unusual in medicine. When the medical team arrived at Marina's room on their morning rounds, I tried to let the doctors know about what happened the previous night, but the medical group was too busy to listen to anything that was not on their immediate agenda. Taking advantage of the short pause, when I was unsuccessfully trying to tell what happened at night, the attending physician asked Marina how she was doing. She answered that she had slept well and that she easily endured today's pain. Hardly she had finished her report when the attending physician declared to the medical group that Marina suffered with a functional pain of an unknown nature, and now she could be discharged home right away.

"But what should I do if my wife's back pain returns? I asked him.

"That is no problem," he answered affably. "Our resident will give you a prescription for morphine in tablets that she can take in case of significant pain."

"Without ten percent dose titration?"

"Yes, without."

"I do not quite understand you, Doctor. Does that mean that when my wife received morphine intravenously, she was allowed a ridiculously slow increase of the morphine dose, but now, when she goes home and will be under much less medical supervision than in the hospital, she can take this painkiller without ridiculous restrictions?"

"I understand your point. You are right. You see, with the raging opioid-related crisis, the government rules require us to manage dose of morphine as we did it with your wife. You see, not us but medical authorities above us establish the rules, and we must obey them," he answered, confirming for me the primary role of medical bureaucracy in today's medical system.

Later that morning, Marina and I returned home, our sweet home. A couple of hours after that, her pain subsided even more. Marina was lucky—though she had countless bone metastases, each of which could be a source of excruciating chronic pain, miraculously, she never suffered from chronic pain. Obviously, the attending physician was right—her pain really belonged to the functional category. I never filled her prescription for morphine, not only because Marina did not have a need for it but also because she was extremely afraid of becoming addicted.

Night Trauma and Unexpected Discovery

In late July 2018, in the middle of a peaceful night, I heard a terrible crash and a scream coming from our bathroom. I ran there and found Marina on the floor groaning and lying helpless. Turning on the light, I saw blood coming from her nose and mouth. Fortunately, she was fully conscious, and it appeared that no bones were broken. Seeing me, she extended her hand to help her to get up. After she was on her feet, she let go of my hand and supporting herself with her arm on the wall slowly got to her bedroom. I offered her a cup of water and taking a few sips, she told me what happened. In the middle of the night, she went to the bathroom. The bathroom was dimly lit by light coming from outside and on the way out from the bathroom, not knowing that both shower doors were open, she extended her arm, trying to lean on one of them. Not finding support, she collapsed onto the floor.

When Marina's superficial bleeding stopped, I examined her body and did not find any visible damage. Then I offered to take her to the ER, but she refused, saying she felt fine and all she wanted now to do was sleep. Very soon her breathing became calm and even, and she fell sound asleep.

Only the next day, we could assess the full scope of her injury. Fortunately, she did not damage her bones or muscles, but there were numerous bruises all over her body, not only from the fall but also as a consequence of the long-term use of a blood thinner, Lovenox, which for many years she self-injected into her abdomen twice daily to prevent thrombotic side effects of chemotherapy.

For the next month, Marina looked terrible. She could hide the bruising on her body with clothes, but the extensive bruising around her eyes and cheeks gave her raccoon appearance.

A couple of days passed, and we went for the regular visit with Dr. Miller. At the sight of Marina's face, Dr. Miller threw up her hands and expressed her sympathy. Then, "just in case," she sent Marina to image department to have an MRI.

When we visited Dr. Miller ten days later, she entered the exam room without saying a word and handed MRI report to us to read. The report was long and had alarming terms, one of which I mistakenly read as "leptomeningitis." The suffix "-itis" means the presence of inflammation. The presence of nonspecific inflammation could be a common phenomenon in any part of the body, and as soon as it is non-symptomatic, it is not of a great clinical importance. Therefore, I did not attach much significance to the finding. Not experienced with neurological lingo, I failed to read that what was written was actually "leptomeninigomatosis," a condition which is associated with any kind of brain tumors. Though I misread the report, nevertheless, I was alarmed with the findings and asked Dr. Miller what she thought about this report.

"All I can say I do not think this report changes anything right now in Marina's treatment. I will not make any changes in her management," her answer was.

"But what is the meaning of all the findings indicated in the report? Does this mean that you and the radiologist saw something dangerous in her brain?" I asked.

"Let's wait a couple of months, then we will repeat the MRI. Comparing it with the original films, we will learn if something has clinical importance.

Do not forget that chemo Marina presently receives still works well on your wife's body," Dr. Miller answered.

Maybe if I had kept asking more questions, I'd get some pretty bad news from our doctor, but as I assumed months later, most probably she did not want to be a messenger of bad news and probably she did not want to alarm my wife and me unnecessarily. In any case, neither Marina nor I learned that day that actually her MRI report showed that she had cancerous metastases in her brain. Only later did I understand the terrible importance of that finding.

Metastatic cancer is a complex condition, and methods of its treatment can be different in the hands of different doctors. I had read plenty of literature on the treatment of metastatic cancer, but the book knowledge about treatment is absolutely not the same as when it is applied in practice of medicine. Not being a specialist in the area of oncology, I knew that my involvement in making important decisions about Marina's treatment might be counterproductive. Anytime a new chemotherapeutic agent was ordered for Marina, lacking deep knowledge of its practical implications, I did not know how effective it might be or what side effects might be expected with its use. In my own field of pediatrics, I was well versed in the choice of various drugs for different conditions, but in the field of oncology, I had only minimal knowledge of what drug worked best for each separate type of malignant condition and its different stages. Thus, completely lost when I tried to figure out what the best treatment for Marina could be, I relied unreservedly on the Marina's oncologists' recommendations. In a way, it was making my own life much easier. Since nothing was dependent on my opinion, I did not need to suffer from doubts about what road might be better to choose when making major decisions about her treatment. Marina, an exemplary patient, trusted the doctors' recommendations even more than I did.

"I Feel Great"

Two months had passed since the 2018 New Year, and I noticed that the eternal youth that usually radiated from Marina had now become the victim of disease and age. She still insisted on performing easy household duties and on attending early-morning religious services. She still was not in pain, and her appetite was tolerable, but now she could drive only short distances and became easily tired after little exertion. She began taking regular naps in the middle of the day, which she had never done before. The disease was affecting Marina's appearance, gradually erasing her natural beauty, dropping its nasty merciless curtain over her lovely appearance, making her look older than she was. Only her eyes, her beautiful, expressive brown eyes, which I never stopped to admire, remained young and alert. Despite undesirable changes still, it was out of the question that my fighter, even with her diminished energy, was going to give up. Once, returning from a successful visit to the doctor, while I was driving, Marina was much more verbose than usual. "You know, Vovka, I am well aware that life can be perceived as a miserable place. Here people are born, many of them suffer, get sick, all grow old, and all die. On the other hand, life can be perceived as a celebration of beautiful words, sounds, and images, all that makes us happy human beings. Well, I deliberately choose to live amidst the celebration of life, and to ignore--as much as it is possible, of course--the dark side of our life. This is my simple philosophy."

She did not lose heart and she was happy to be present on the life's fair. She sharply limited her walks but continued to perform most of the activities she had done before, though it took her longer to carry out them. Sometimes I caught her carrying a heavy laundry basket upstairs from the basement, where our washer and dryer were situated. I firmly repeated to her many times that she should let me do this kind of work, especially because of her compromised bones. I hadn't even finished my sentence when she would strongly take my hand away from the heavy laundry basket and with a stubborn "No" continued climbing slowly toward our second-floor bedrooms. Nevertheless, there were now days when she reluctantly allowed me to take care of the tasks that needed significant effort.

Even with all these negative changes, when our friends called and asked her how she felt, she continued to invariably respond with a cheerful "Perfect!" which she pronounced with gusto and sincere enthusiasm.

"Marina, why do you say 'perfect' when you feel so tired?" I would ask her.

In response followed the same answer I had heard for all these long years. "Oh, here you go again. Why cannot you understand such simple thing, Vovka? In the first place, I could feel much worse than I feel right now, and second, my complaints cannot change anything anyway. And I don't want anyone to take pity on me."

Dermatologist in Tight Pants

In February 2018, a new unpleasant development awaited us. It started when Marina noticed that the skin lesions below her breast area, instead of vanishing as Dr. Miller had predicted, were now actually getting worse. Marina did not betray any concern. After years and years of the incessant barrage of bad news, we silently agreed not to worry too much about the new lesions, at least not until she next went to see her oncologist.

A week later when Dr. Miller examined Marina, she referred her to another dermatologist who specialized in oncological cases. Marina got an appointment with her two days later.

The dermatologist was a beautiful young woman. Her radiation of the boundless immortality of youth could give the impression that the doctor had only recently started to practice her specialty. This pretty doctor was the embodiment of an ideal modern woman. Instead of wearing a doctor's lab coat, she was dressed in sporty pants, a lovely light white blouse, and trendy sports shoes. If not for the medical office environment, we could think that we came to see not a doctor but a fitness instructor or a model. Before us was a highly educated professional, who at the same time gave the impression of a perfect robot. It seemed as though she lived in the world different from her visitors. Her way of dealing with a patient was as if the patient was an inanimate, obedient toy, or, better, as if the patient was an inanimate object that she was going to examine and possibly fix. While without doubts the doctor had received a perfect education in dermatology, it was obvious that nobody had ever taught her that patients are human beings who can think and feel.

Finishing her examination of the skin lesions, still not saying a single word, the dermatologist entered the results of her observations into the computer and then she uttered her first phrase during the visit that she was going to perform a skin biopsy. This procedure took only a few minutes. On our way out, the dermatologist said that Marina did not need to come back to her. She said that in ten days when the results of the biopsy would be available, Dr. Miller's office will call Marina for the next appointment.

Marina never lost her sense of humor. "You made a big mistake by not becoming a dermatologist, my friend," she told me on the way home. "Not only because nobody calls you in the middle of the night or that you do not need to rush to the ER at all hours of the day, but mainly because you do not need to rack your brain over the diagnosis. Just perform a biopsy, and ten days later, a pathologist from the laboratory will inform you what the diagnosis is."

Dr. Miller's office called us in the due time, and Marina and I went to see our oncologist to discuss the results of the skin biopsy. Prior to this visit, Marina mentioned to me not once that she already knew her skin lesions result would be positive for a progressing malignancy, but also that this result did not bother her much. "Don't I have multiple metastases already?" my unfailing optimist rationalized. "So what? Why worry? One more or one less—what is the difference? I am sure our doctor will find one way or another to deal with my skin problem, as she did before. In any case," she finished, "why should I worry of something that does not change the essence of the main problem?"

Less by One Metastasis

Dr. Miller entered the room, warmly greeted us, and, just as Marina expected, told her that the biopsy revealed her skin lesions were breast cancer metastases. Marina was not expressing any emotions. After so many years of bad news, it seemed that she had come to the point where she was mentally anesthetized to bad news.

"I think that the medications you are taking now will continue to serve you well," said Dr. Miller. "Instead of replacing them with something else, it would be better if you instead had a radiation treatment for this type of metastases."

Radiation treatment of Marina's skin lesions started two days later. Prior to the treatment, Marina was examined by the department's physician, who in detail explained the impending therapy. Asking many questions, Marina, whose mind was clear and intact, actively took part in the conversation.

The presence of other people in the waiting room of the radiation depart-ment had a calming effect on Marina. Almost all the patients were accom-panied by a supportive relative or friend--another reminder that the world abounds with good people. The treatment consisted of several sessions of radiation. Each treatment session lasted for minutes. Sitting in the comfort-able waiting room, I was surprised by the number of people who needed the department's services. The department worked like clockwork. Each patient was called in to receive their treatment precisely at the exact time of their ap-pointment. The staff and doctors of the radiation department who worked there were exemplary professionals, humane, and friendly.

When the course of radiation treatments was coming to an end, Marina had the next appointment with the department's doctor. Satisfied with the results of the radiation, he recommended an added course of treatment this time with infrared light. The heat produced by infrared light serves as an added element in the destruction of malignant cells. This method of treat-ment was not used often, and the last time it was used in the department had been more than a year earlier.

Implementation of this kind of therapy required the use of expensive machinery and time expenditure by those who serviced it. Medical insur-ance does not pay for the procedure, but in the best traditions of generos-ity, which is so often found in this country, the treatment was provided to Marina for free.

Apart from lack of energy and weakness, Marina's general health remained surprisingly good. She tolerated the entire course of treatment in the radiation department without any side effects.

Thanks to the radiation therapy, in a short time, Marina's lesions practically disappeared. The positive outcome helped to raise our spirits, and though it seemed that presently Marina's entire body was stuffed of cancerous metastases, it gave us a renewed reason to hope that at least for the foreseeable future, these metastases might be successfully controlled.

From the Fair of Life. Goodbye Winnie-the-Pooh, Goodbye Piglet . . .

It was unfortunate but inevitable that sooner or later our miracles were coming to an end. A month later, after the treatment of skin metastases was successfully finished, things went south. Marina's appetite disappeared, and her level of strength and energy was decreasing from one day to the next.

During one of our appointments, Marina asked Dr. Miller if her decreasing energy had anything to do with the findings on her brain MRI. Exactly as it was months earlier, Dr. Miller did not directly answer Marina's question; she just shook her head in the negative.

It was the first time during our life together that Marina did not resist my suggestions to help her with the household duties. Under her guidance, I gradually mastered the art of cooking. The housecleaning continued to be performed by a reliable team of cleaning ladies twice a month.

Marina still went to synagogue for morning and, now rarely, for Sabbath services. It was difficult for her to wake up as early as before and it required more and more time for her preparations to go outside. She often arrived at the synagogue after the service had already started. With all this, she never forgot to take meticulous care of herself. Dressed in elegant clothing, she always appeared attractive and distinct. Since I knew her, she never used any makeup, except a lipstick sometimes, but she now liked to wear stylish jewelry.

Marina, who now ate only a limited number of meals, did not like the food that was served in the synagogue after religious services. Instead, before the service, she drove to the local Dunkin' Donuts store to buy from there her favorite cappuccino coffee and either plain or Boston cream donuts, which later she ate together with the rest of the group after the service.

Other than reading books, Marina's main cultural entertainment became the Chicago Lyric Opera. She loved classical opera and tried not to miss a single performance. We went downtown by car and took advantage of the underground level of Poetry Parking, which was conveniently located across the street from the Lyric Opera. Realizing how slow she had become, Marina started her preparation for the performance hours before it began. We would come downtown half an hour before the performance, park the car, and take the elevator to the street level of the building. Then Marina, refusing my help, from time to time leaning on the wall to support her, slow but with unbending determination, would walk in the direction of the Opera Theater. At the theater during performances, Marina would completely forget about the brutal challenges of life and, full of emotion, sit immersed in the magical power of operatic masterpieces.

From time to time, we also attended the concerts of Russian singers and, less often, American musicals. The last concert she attended was on September 17, 2018. The performer was a popular Russian singer, Mikhail Shufutinsky. Marina, on the threshold of life's end, enjoyed his performance as much as the rest of the audience, and she did not miss a single opportunity to applaud. Such is the power of music, and such was the unbendable warrior who was my wife.

Though Marina was gradually losing energy level, it did not reflect on her mood, and complaining was not in her repertoire. She visited doctors, she worked on the computer, she cheerfully spoke on the phone with members of our family and friends, she studied Hebrew, and she listened to her favorite music. When she did not have enough strength for her usual activities, reading remained her constant powerful healer. The process of reading hardly ever tired her. Using her Kindle, she usually read while sitting in her favorite armchair or a La-Z-Boy.

Marina's mind remained alert and clear, but now she rarely started a conversation, though she did not hesitate much to participate in one. Each day she went deeper into herself. I understood perfectly well what was happening with her and that it could not be otherwise. She spoke less not because she was depressed—she never was depressed—but because she was carefully saving her energy. Our last exchange of baby-like talk had happened in February 2018. We had been in the car, driving home when, completely out of blue, Marina had a mental lapse from reality and, in the middle of our conversation, unexpectedly changed her tone. Just like in our good old times, she began to speak with me as if she were a funny Piglet and I was her faithful Winnie-the-Pooh. Our conversation in this manner lasted maybe five minutes, after which she became silent and went back into herself. Everything comes to an end, and it was the last time when we indulged in our childish talk. After that, for no money in the world, she would return to our favorite pastime.

Marina's appetite continued to worsen. Now she ate only freshly cooked food and refused to eat processed food. I did my best to find things she would not reject, but my culinary skills were limited, and soon we hired a woman who at the beginning of the day prepared meals for Marina at our home. Each morning, I drove to Panera Bread to buy her favorite sourdough bread from there.

In the declining whirlwind of her disease, Marina managed to remain a caring wife. When I deserved it, she was critical of my appearance. She watched that I was well shaved, that I had a haircut on time, that I wore proper attire, that I changed my shirts daily, and that everything about me was clean and neat. She herself did not miss a single visit to the beauty parlor for a manicure and pedicure.

A time eventually came when she hardly ever asked me what was going on with me. There were no more words of her encouraging and caring compliments in my address that emotionally I had needed to hear so much many times a day in the past. The relentless and merciless attack of her inner enemy was doing its job. It forced Marina to be focused on herself while she was going through the trials that befell her. Now all her remaining energy was used to fight the cancer's ever-progressing efforts to take away her life.

After July 2018, Marina's condition did not change much, except that day after day, she was further losing her appetite and becoming increasingly tired. It was sad to acknowledge that despite all our efforts, her cancer continued to do its devastating work. Looking at her each day, I saw my recently youthful wife transform from a shining beauty to . . . let's say "a senior citizen." Yet in spite of everything, though I clearly saw on Marina's face the encroaching features of older age, thanks to some unknown to me psychological mechanism, my eyes and my mind transformed the reality, and I saw her as healthy and happy. I was able to travel back in time and see my Marina as she looked when we met more than half a century ago. Magically, my imagination successfully smoothed all the wrinkles and bags on her face, and I saw my wife as young and beautiful as many years before. Love is an untamed force. Being a pediatrician, I saw many times the embodiments of love when mothers who were caressing their children with serious congenital defects reflected on their external appearance. Undisguised bright love flashed in their eyes when they were caring for their beloved, but severely deformed by nature, children.

Following our long-time ritual, Marina and I met at the kitchen table for a meal three times a day. The topics of our conversations could be different, but they hardly ever touched on anything that had to do with the final exit from this world. My deep and everlasting hope that currently used course of chemotherapy would miraculously change the course of Marina's condition remained intact. Each time our car reached the stretch of the road from our home to the expressway, I made a mental note that I was driving together with my Marina along our Road of Hope.

Usually, when we drove from the oncologist's office after unfavorable changes in Marina's imaging studies, we would be silent, not showing emotions, immersed in our own thoughts. Marina looked at the road before her while I was praying that today's results were not as bad as they might appear. Mentally protesting the disturbing news, I clenched my fists, ready to resume a new fight against the devious and vicious inner enemy. However, when the results that we heard at the appointment were satisfactory, *joie de vivre*, happiness and hope returned to us; our anxiety would be gone, and we would be in a positive mood.

Collateral Damage

The lives of people who live together for a long time, whether they like it or not, become tightly intertwined in various aspects. This is especially clear when their relationship is put to test by inevitable misfortunes. For many years, I suffered from gastrointestinal problems, and following the axiom that the stomach is the seat of all feeling, the more Marina's problems progressed to the worse, the more my own health problem manifested in the form of severe heartburn and abdominal discomfort. Doctors of various medical specialties explained to me that the cause for my symptoms was my advanced age and my hiatal hernia. In a hiatal hernia, the upper part of the stomach bulges through the diaphragm into the chest cavity. Not questioning doctors' conclusion, I humbly questioned them if there was a possibility that my condition had to do with the emotional stress related to my wife's condition. To this question, I never received a clear-cut, positive response. The unenthusiastic reply was always similar to the one I had received many years ago before I had open-heart surgery, asking cardiologists if my chest pain might be related to mental stress and anxiety. In one voice, the specialists assured me that emotional problems were of secondary importance in real somatic diseases. When I heard that science-based medicine did not believe in a direct relationship between physical illness and spiritual well-being, I could not ignore that my own life experience told me a different story. What's more, literature, and the life experiences of various people I have communicated with, have confirmed my notion that many physical symptoms happen when a person is exposed to different types of stress. The best proof that emotions affected my stomach is that now, three years after Marina, my friend, left me, my gastrointestinal problems are hardly manifesting.

Meanwhile, Marina's cancer often produced its own new and unpleasant symptoms. In the morning or the evening, she would call me to her room and tell me about another new warning sign she experienced. In most cases, it was a minor problem, but after the earlier dramatic trials and tribulations, being a physician, each time I examined her, I imagined the worst—the beginning of an infection, or a fracture, or a new metastasis. Whenever I imagined that she had developed a new, potentially dangerous medical problem, I felt a burning pain under my ribs in my stomach area, which forced me to take a handful of Tums or Sodium Bicarbonate tablets in addition to a prescription drug. At the same time, along with the abdominal issues, I began to have a vague pain in my chest. Since the chest pain's location coincided with position of my heart, I was alarmed that it could be related to my previous angina pectoris episode that had been treated in 1995 with open-heart surgery. Eventually though for Marina, my presence as a caregiver was—I could say—critical, she insisted that I must go to the ER of the university hospital. Although it was the middle of September in 2018, a month and a half before she left this world, she insisted on going with me to the ER, which she did. From the ER, I was admitted to the hospital.

The next day, the hospital's GI team refused to work me up when they learned that I'd had cardiac surgery in the past. They explained to me that before taking care of my GI problems, they needed to rule out that my gastrointestinal symptoms could be caused primarily by cardiac issues. In the best spirit of American medicine, two days later, I had an angiography that established that after the quintuple-bypass open-heart surgery performed twenty-three years ago, now three of my coronary arteries had become completely occluded. Acting on this data, right away after angiography, on the same operation table, the interventional cardiologist inserted stents in two of my occluded coronary arteries. After the procedure, the same cardiologist told me that in a month, I would receive one more stent in the yet-occluded third coronary artery.

During restoration of the circulation in my coronary arteries, my devoted best friend, my suffering servant, Marina, despite her own precarious condition, was among other family members in the waiting room, awaiting the outcome of the procedure. Subsequently, despite my strong protests,

Marina visited me daily after the surgery. Four days after admission, I was discharged from the hospital in improved condition.

When I returned home, as before, I resumed care for Marina, but while I was taking prescribed antiacid medications, vague abdominal symptoms still seriously interfered with my health. The number of antacids I needed to control my symptoms increased every day, but I did my best not to bother Marina with my problems.

Meanwhile, her condition quickly deteriorated. Now that her cancer was raising its ugly head higher and higher, she managed to perform only basic household chores. With my help, she made sure everything in the house was clean and fresh. She continued to attend weekday religious services, she called and received calls from friends, and she did not part with her Kindle.

One evening in October 2018, three weeks after the two stents had been inserted in my coronary arteries, I experienced bad chest pain. Accompanied by Marina, my son, and his wife, I went back to the emergency room at the same hospital and was at once admitted for further treatment. Before Marina went home, I beseeched her not to visit me while I was in the hospital.

Once again, I was under management of the cardiac team, and in impressive spirit of the remarkable efficiency of American medicine, the very next day, I received another stent placed in the obstructed coronary vessel. Despite my active protests, my long-suffering, devoted wife, my guardian angel, visited me in the hospital every day. Twice she used Uber, and once our son brought her to the hospital. When she arrived by Uber, one of the hospital's employees--each time different--usually a transporter, seeing Marina walking unsteadily through the lobby toward the elevators, caught up with her with a wheelchair and wheeled her into my hospital room.

As before, each time when unannounced, Marina would appear at the door of my hospital room; I implored her repeatedly not to visit me, but it was useless. Despite her low energy level, in a quiet but firm like a steel voice--though monotonous--she objected, saying that she would do what she considered to be right. To persuade this woman was impossible. The indescribable irony was that now it was not me, but she, who did not forget to tell me that everything would be fine.

Every cloud has a silver lining. In my case if not for the abdominal problems that had bothered me for many years of my life, and became intolerable due to worries about Marina's health, I would never have been admitted to the hospital and would never have received the stents that helped me so remarkably in the future. Indeed, in the best possible scenario, if I had complained about abdominal discomfort and chest pain to my regular doctor, he would have referred me to a cardiologist, who would have definitely ordered me to perform a heart stress test. But I'd had such stress tests several times almost annually in the past, and they never revealed any problem with my heart. It was only due to the university cardiologists' suspicion that something serious was happening with my heart that I was able to bypass the less meaningful cardiac tests and was taken straight to the cardiac lab. The angiography that was performed there revealed my obstructed coronary vessels and right away mentioned two stents and later one more stent were inserted. "Refurbished" heart potentially added healthy years to my life. Several months later, thanks to the three inserted stents in my heart, vague cardiac pain and discomfort related to it stopped bothering me. The unplanned cardiac surgery helped me feel stronger and younger. It was a real victory.

The Forces Are Unequal, but the Struggle Does Not Stop

Unfortunately, the good news related to my health was the opposite of what was happening to Marina's health. From the moment I returned home after my second hospitalization, her tiredness, lack of energy, and hesitant gait only increased. Her hearing got much worse as well. On the morning of October 17, 2018, the day after my discharge from the hospital, on our way to morning religious service, going from the house to the garage, I noticed that Marina walked with much more noticeable hesitance and unsteady gait, with one hand holding on to the jacket she was wearing and with the other the arm stretched out in front of her—which reminded me of the same picture when our eleven-month-old son, taking his first steps, was hanging on to his clothes.

"Marina, what's wrong? Why are you holding yourself when you walk?" I asked her.

"I do not know myself," she answered, smiling at me with a charming and apologetic smile, as if she were a small girl.

Only four unfortunate days later, I received long-awaited explanation not only for Marina's poorly balanced gait, but for her optical illusion she had when she thought I had driven too close to the edge of my lane.

The physician in me should have known that an unsteady gait could be a sign of a serious health problem, but the other part of me steadily denied thinking about bad scenarios. Even seeing the obvious serious troubles with Marina's health with my own eyes, for no money in the world would I lose my hope that sooner or later the chemo would do its job and we would be out of woods. It was not the first time when Marina had gone through a difficult period in her life, and not the first time when like a mythical bird Phoenix, she would rise from ashes and continue to enjoy life.

The main inner organs of Marina's body, including those that were affected by cancer, were functioning well; she was not depressed, and to a significant extent, she was still independent. At this twilight time, it was encouraging that she continued to sleep well, did not suffer from pain, and was still enjoying reading. Many hours she spent sitting comfortably in her favorite armchair, forgetting of everything, while holding faithful Kindle device in her hands, and, as if nothing happened, reading another book. Reading, a true blessing, was now her main refuge against the aggressive cancerous metastases attacking her body on so many fronts.

Facing Marina's gradually increasing weakness, we returned with more urgency than in the past to an issue that we had discussed before between us. Since for her it was increasingly difficult to climb the stairs to her bedroom on the second floor, it was logical that the best way to solve this problem was by installing a mechanical stair lift. However, our discussion halted when Marina decidedly told me that she did not want any aid climbing the stairs, not until the time comes when she could not do so on her own. For her, being independent was an indicator that things were not as bad as they seemed. Indeed, with stubborn determination, she continued to climb the stairs slowly and resolutely to the second floor. The plan to obtain the stair lift was put off and was never implemented.

Now the woman we'd hired to do different chores in our house came almost every day. Her main responsibility remained to prepare food that would please Marina's poor appetite.

Marina attended a religious service for the last time at the end of October 2018. Her life force gradually decreased, and this time our expectation that she would get better did not come true. Despite all her efforts to eat more food, she was unable to do so. Any food that she was offered, her body refused to accept. Nutritional shakes such as Ensure and Boost were out of the question; they were too sweet for her and produced a heartburn. When I asked Marina for the reasons she was refusing food, she either blamed on a feeling of nausea and heartburn, or most often, she just shrugged and did not answer at all. To me, her gesture meant that she could not explain to someone who was in good health her aversion to food. The medication for nausea, Ondansetron (Zofran), which had been effective for many years, now hardly helped her.

With all Marina's problems, she continued to enjoy telephone calls from family and friends. And as it was many times before, when they asked about her health, in a strong and cheerful voice, she answered with the same short triumphal "Perfect."

The Last Visit to the Emergency Room

It was October 20, 2018, when Marina's symptoms drastically worsened. She practically stopped eating, and her weakness became more pronounced. As a rule, during any significant decline in her condition, I would offer to take her to the emergency room for evaluation, which she usually refused, telling me it was all temporary, that she would improve soon, and most often, she hated to go to the hospital. However, this time she said nothing and began to prepare herself for the drive. She did not belong to the category of people who could afford to think about capitulation. If somebody had told her this might be the last car ride in her life, she would have just shrugged and said nothing. Having faith in her own strength, she continued to take life as it was, and when she could not change anything with her own actions, she courageously followed her destiny.

The inner strength of this woman never ceased to amaze me. During critical moments of her illness when she would learn about presence of new metastases, or about necessity for hospital treatment, she never tried to share her thoughts with me or with anybody else. On these occasions she did not cry and did not ask for support. Like a brave soldier she silently and courageously confronted the most unpleasant news.

Gathering all the things she might need when she was admitted to the hospital, we left the house. Without my support, Marina on her own reached our detached garage. A feeling of painful sadness filled me when our car drove down our Road of Hope. This time the voice of hope lurked in the far recesses of my chest. On the way to the emergency room, we did not speak. When we drove up to the entrance, my heartburn flared to such a degree that I felt like a Niagara Falls of acid was flowing inside of my stomach. Thankfully, from earlier similar situations, I was aware of such a possibility. From my pants pocket, I took a good handful of Tums and Sodium Bicarbonate tablets, pushed them into my mouth, chewed them swiftly, and washed them down with a bottle of water I carried with me in the car.

Leaving the car in the emergency parking, I went with Marina to the door of the emergency room. When I extended my arm to help her, with a gesture, she let me know that she wanted to walk in on her own. Then, moving slowly, she took a seat in one of the many wheelchairs that stood inside the room.

Leaving her, I quickly went to park the car. When I returned to the ER, I found her patiently sitting, waiting to be admitted. She was silent, pale, and at the same time surprisingly calm. I sat on the chair next to her, expecting that she might need my help. My ever-present hope burned in me with a weak flickering flame. I could not admit to myself that the battle for the life of my beloved friend of fifty-six years' union might be lost.

There were many people in the ER waiting to be admitted. When I approached a nurse at the desk and asked her when Marina would be taken to one of the exam rooms, she told me she was fully aware of Marina's condition and that she would be admitted soon. Indeed, in less than ten minutes, we were ushered in. Marina looked and behaved much differently from her normal behavior. She was silent and did not show any interest in conversation, but there was no fear or anxiety in her appearance. Looking at her, it was clear she was fully reconciled with her fate. She reminded me of a person who sits on a boat without oars, detached from the world around her, obediently going where the trusted water current takes her.

The usual ER routine began. First Marina was examined by a nurse who took her history and vital signs, after which the ER physician came in. Attentive and polite, he asked Marina several questions, which, after a short pause, she answered clearly and adequately. Finishing the exam, before he left the room, he told us that among other tests, he had ordered a CT scan of Marina's brain, and he would return when the result was ready. When he was ready to leave, Marina perked up a little. She opened her eyes and for a moment appeared better than when we arrived. Then, too tired to speak with me, she again closed her weary eyes while I resumed reading a newspaper that I'd brought with me from home. Shortly, the CT technician with an assistant came in to take her to the X-ray room. They moved her from the hospital bed to a gurney and on it they transported her to the imaging department. After quarter an hour, she was brought back to the examining room. When she was put back in bed, she opened her eyes, looked at me for a fleeting moment, and then, closing her eyes, disconnected herself from the outside world.

It did not take long for the ER physician to reappear to the examining room. When he came in, Marina once again opened her eyes and looked at him questioningly. The doctor did not keep us waiting. Casually and without a hint of drama, he had informed Marina and me that on the CT brain scan he saw two significant-sized metastatic tumors in the cerebellum and signs of leptomeninigomatosis. When he finished talking, I realized that I had heard the worst news in my life. As for Marina, having listened to this formidable news, she said nothing; she just barely slightly nodded her head and closed her eyes. After a minute passed, during which I was not able to say a word, I asked the ER physician what will happen next. He answered that Marina would be hospitalized for further diagnosis and treatment.

When he left the room, I took Marina's hand and squeezed it lightly. She opened her eyes, looked at me, and had a courage and strength to tell me, to the healthy one, that I should not worry. "Relax, Vovka, everything will be all right," she told me in a weak but firm like an iron tone of voice. "Call our children with the news." Then, after a long pause, she added, "Stop worrying. We will break through."

By this time, we had dealt with metastases all over Marina's body—in her breasts, in her bones, her liver, her lungs, her skin, and now cancer showed itself in her brain. *What are we are going to do with brain metastasis*, I thought, still not understanding that we had reached the end of the road.

There, in the emergency room, came the time when I was able to clearly put together and decipher the unexplainable events that had happened over the past year. All the puzzles were solved in a short instant. So, the tumor in the cerebellum had been responsible for Marina's earlier loss of balance, for manifesting in her hesitant and unsteady gait, and for the episode when she thought I was not driving in my lane. It also became clear that the unusual progression of Marina's hearing loss was certainly associated with the brain tumor. Her fall in the bathroom two months ago in all probability was due to her compromised sense of balance.

It was already midnight when a transporter aide came to take Marina in a wheelchair to her assigned room, escorting us through a labyrinth of underground corridors that connected several hospital buildings. I walked next to her, holding her hand, holding my chin up.

In the Hospital Room

Marina's hospital room was comfortable, clean, and supplied with all kinds of advanced technological devices. She got up from the wheelchair by herself and refusing my help, by herself climbed into bed. Saying nothing, she at once fell in a blessed sleep, even while the nurse restarted her IV. She slept soundly all night.

When she awoke at six o'clock in the morning, she had not improved much from the previous day, though in the past after receiving IV fluids, her condition usually improved. For her last days, she entered a stage of human existence that could not be understood by those who have never had a serious problem with their health.

In June 1995, twenty-three years earlier, I had experienced hard way a striking transformation in my own outlook on life. In the midst of complete health, I woke up one night with terrible chest pain accompanied with an inner high-voltage electric current painfully shaking my chest, left jaw, and left arm. Even if I were not a doctor, I would understand that I had a case of severe angina. Marina, awakened by my agonal screams, took me to the emergency room, where I was diagnosed as a cardiac patient and was at once transferred to the ICU unit. The next day, angiography was performed that showed five coronary arteries obstructions in my heart. Thanks to the incredible American medicine (I must repeat this definition though I did it over and over again), on the next day, I had my quintuple-bypass open-heart surgery.

It was remarkable how during this serious challenge in my life, I had a feeling that my body was transferred from the live compartment of healthy people to the live compartment of people severely incapacitated by an illness. The fundamental feature of this transformation was loss of the intrinsic quality of healthy individuals to fight for life. I was fully aware that a severe degree of illness might affect a recently healthy organism so profoundly that instead of a desire to live, the only choice left to critically sick patients is to submit to expecting their destiny.

I clearly remember that, afflicted with angina, in brutal pain, instead of resisting the sickness, all I'd wanted was just to be able to breathe, and nothing else. *Just let me breathe*; it was all I wanted. This state of health, which lasted for days, taught me that when a person has the strength to resist, to complain, to yell, to demand, that person is not really sick. A really sick person does not have enough energy or words to express their suffering but lies detached from what is happening around him, surrendered to the force of destiny, disengaged from fight for life.

Now that same farewell-to-arms state of mind has happened to my fighter, my fearless heroine, my dear wife. It appeared as if Marina was ready to be ferried by the mythical Charon from the shores of Life to the shores of the incomprehensible state of Underworld. She was still with those who were alive, but at the same time, she already belonged to the eternal part of reality.

On the morning of the second day of her admission, after waking up, Marina appeared slightly better than before. She felt stronger, and the nausea and heartburn she had suffered the previous day did not bother her as much as they had before. Unexpectedly for me, she was able to eat some of the breakfast she ordered by herself—yes, by herself—from the hospital kitchen early that morning. Forgetting about the previous day's nightmare, a thin ray of deceptive hope began to flare up in my heart, and I started to regain my so wishful, and so infinitely irrational optimism.

Alas, very soon the attending physician and, accompanying him, a group of residents and students arrived in the room for morning rounds, returning me to the raw reality. Marina, though appearing tired and exhausted, was awake and alert, weak but adequately answering their questions. However, today she did not have any of her own questions. Facing the impending shutdown of her vital organs and systems, a time came for her to lose her inner impulse to worry about taking care of her life.

I refused to come to terms with the thought that soon I would lose my best friend. Still not completely losing hope, I asked the attending physician if anything else could be done for my wife. The physician only shrugged pointedly and told me that everything that could be done had already been done.

Thinking more with my heart than with my brain, I followed the medical group into the corridor, like a dog with a tail between legs, with a desire to ask another question, but then suddenly I finally understood that nothing could help my life companion. It dawned on me that, like a drowning man who clings to a straw, I was looking for magic that medicine did not have. When I returned to the room, Marina was already done with her breakfast. Now that it had finally reached my consciousness that I was on the threshold of losing my alter ego, before it was too late, I tried to find the most important words that I wanted to tell her. But I could not come up with anything other than just repeating the same phrase that I loved her more than anything in the world. As for Marina, under the detrimental influence of the terminal illness, she was losing her life force, and now all she could do was to concentrate on seeing in her mind the fast-receding signposts along the long road of life.

Radiation Oncologist Visit

Each of the following days brought worse news. There were no new symptoms, but the symptoms that already existed got steadily worse. On the fourth day in the hospital, Marina had a visit from a radiation oncologist. This middle-aged doctor was an extraordinary beautiful woman who belonged to the special category of physicians who helped those people who were entering the narrow minefield between life and death. The doctor told Marina that the purpose of her visit was to hear Marina's decision about what she wanted to do with the management of her brain's malignant lesions. With an impenetrable facial expression that did not betray feelings and showed impeccable professionalism, the doctor told that the only possible treatment for Marina's brain cancer was radiotherapy of the brain. Marina, fully awake and amazingly lucid, was listening very attentively about the offered treatment, and when the doctor paused, Marina, in a voice devoid of emotion, asked her what was needed from her in the current situation.

"This is exactly what I was planning to discuss with you tomorrow," the doctor answered. "But as long as you are asking me this today, we can deal with it right away. I have only one question for you. Are you willing to have radiation treatment?"

"Tell me about the side effects of radiation therapy in more details, please," Marina said, emphatically trying to sound firm and rational.

"That is exactly what I want you to know," the radiation oncologist said, her beautiful face taking on a serious expression. With all her professionalism, the doctor could not hide her humanity at that moment. "I must tell you that there are many side effects from radiation of the brain. It affects your appetite and makes you nauseous. Your head feels like it has been squashed in a vice. You might have headaches, be dizzy, weak, and feel extreme fatigue. However, the most undesirable effect of radiation therapy is memory loss. We have a special therapy for helping with that, but the effect varies from patient to patient, so we cannot guarantee you a positive result."

"I understand," Marina said in a voice that was weak but still determined and highly rational. "So that's it. It's the end of the road. I want to be myself to the end. Thirteen years of living with cancer is more than enough. I had a wonderful life and now it came time for me to say goodbye."

Marina's words hit me like a heavy brick wall. All that was left for me at this moment was to say farewell to all the hopes of the last years. It was a dead end in the full sense of the word. Medicine was powerless to help my wife, and there was no way to fight the cancer further.

When the radiation oncologist left the room, Marina was very tired, and I felt the invisible thread that had connected us for so many years now partially changed from real reality to a virtual reality. There was silence in the room. Any words were out of place now. Marina was moving away from the world of the living to the world of the unknown, hopefully--as was my dream--to the world of angels.

Soon after the radiation oncologist left, no one other than Dr. Miller came to visit Marina. At the sight of her familiar face, Marina cheered up and even smiled twice during their conversation. It was a weak smile, but a real smile of a thinking person. Marina, a strong woman, had withstood all kinds of metastases, and brain tumors were about to take her life, but they were unable to take away her mind and her spirit. Cancer could destroy her body, but it could not break the strength of her spirit.

CHAPTER 6

In Hospice Care Unit

The Destiny Is Sealed

The next day brought another sad milestone in Marina's life. On the next day after she refused radiation treatment, the attending physician said that tomorrow he was planning to discharge her home where she was going to receive hospice care.

Trying to remain calm and not to lose control over myself, I thought about the practical implications of the doctor's decision. If Marina came home tomorrow for hospice, that meant she would need the visitation by a nurse and she would need to have available all kinds of medical equipment, including a hospital bed, a commode, and a variety of other elements of care for a patient in her position. The doctor whom I asked about it answered that I should not worry; the hospice care company would supply all that was necessary at the same day my wife arrived home.

When Marina fell asleep, I called the woman who was coming to prepare food at our house. When she heard what was happening, she agreed to help me with hospice care for Marina.

After an hour of sleep, Marina awoke, and not I but she was the one who started a short conversation. No, she did not speak about the upcoming hospice treatment. Instead, in this most critical moment of her life, this woman of duty discussed with me practical issues for which she still felt responsibility. First asking how I felt and whether I had eaten today, she told me about household bills that I needed to pay, a faucet that needed repair, and about things that were needed to be bought from the grocery store when she arrived home.

The more I thought about home hospice care, the more I became concerned. I was not worried because I was very exhausted and because I was not certain if I could rely on outside help. Those problems were solvable. The major problem was peculiar specifically to my personality. I knew that in taking care of Marina, full of desire to do the utmost best for her and being a physician, I would constantly and pathologically feel guilty that I had failed to do for her everything that was necessary to satisfy her needs, that I didn't do everything right. Not being able to provide the best possible level of perfect care that my wife deserved in the last hours of her life, I knew that I would feel guilty each passing second. As never before, I felt the truth in the advice given to doctors from time immemorial to not treat their own close relatives. I was sure that being in charge of supplying the best care for Marina, who was leaving this world, would kill me emotionally in the first place. Then I realized that whatever I would plan in the present situation, nothing depended on my decision. With this thought, I chose to surrender to the will of fate.

On the Road to Hospice

It was late afternoon on the same day when a nurse from the hospice company JourneyCare called me in Marina's hospital room. She told me that all necessary medical equipment for hospice care would be delivered to my house early morning tomorrow. I thanked the nurse and told her that with my wife presently being in critical condition, I could not leave her alone in the hospital. If she would be discharged tomorrow, she would not be home until the afternoon. "I must be with her to provide moral and physical support all the time until she arrives to our home. Up to that time, there isn't anyone to open the door for the delivery of medical equipment."

I was in the middle of my explanation, when the nurse interrupted me and told me she would call me in a short time.

It was October 25, the fifth day of Marina's admission to the hospital when at 3:00 p.m., when in vain I was trying to help Marina to eat, a woman came in. It was the same nurse from JorneyCare hospice I just spoke on the phone. Instead of calling, she'd decided to come by the room. I stopped feeding Marina and she at once fell asleep.

"Would you agree if instead of home-based hospice we transfer your wife to a hospice unit at Rush Hospital this evening?" going straight to the subject, the nurse asked me politely.

I was in seventh heaven. Yes, there is God! Oh yes, there is God in the world! God had heard my innermost desire. What the nurse offered me was something I could not even have dreamed. The idea of caring for Marina at home, whom I loved so much, when she said goodbye to life, seeing her life slip away and being helpless to change the course of natural events, satisfying all the details of care she might need, was an impossible task for my psyche to deal with. At the same time, providing a hospice with the best possible professional care would be an ideal solution for the love of my life. Knowing that my wife would be surrounded by professional twenty-four-hour care in a unit specially designed for patients who were there for in the same predicament as Marina was one of the best gifts in life I now had an opportunity to receive. I thanked the nurse, who will never know how grateful I was for her offer. In conclusion the nurse explained to me the details of the transfer.

When she left, I gently woke Marina, who was now in two worlds—one where I was and the other beyond understanding of the outsider—and explained what had been planned for her at the end of this day. Though she was enveloped in the tentacles of ruthless and unappeasable cancer, she listened attentively and nodded her head in response.

The time had come when it was necessary to start preparing for the move to the hospice. For the first time in my life, it was not Marina, but I who was doing the packing. A nurse came to disconnect the IV unit that

Marina would never need again, and now she lay in her bed, still beautiful in my eyes, with her mind intact. She had no pain, and she did not suffer from serious inconveniences. If not for the cancer, she could be a healthy and strong person.

Early in the evening, the ambulance service dispatcher called me to say that in an hour paramedics would arrive to take Marina to the hospice. She told me that I must drive there by my own car and then explained how to get to the place where Marina would be brought. Just in case, she provided me with the address of the hospice.

Those unfortunate people who have been in my place will understand how painfully and tearfully the heart of the life partner is aching, realizing that a person with whom he or she has spent many precious years of life has now embarked on last journey, a journey from which there is no return. I was one of those innumerable people before me who would be glad if destiny took them instead of their loved one. Those who have really loved will agree with me without hesitation.

It was already dark outside when paramedics arrived in Marina's hospital room. Her pale face did not express a hint of fear or anxiety when she saw them. Submitting to fate, she was calm and tired, and only her eyes showed that her mind was thoughtful and alert.

The paramedics, two strong young women with good professional skills, easily transferred Marina's obedient body from the hospital bed to the gurney.

"The place where we are taking Marina is difficult to find," one of the ambulance technicians reminded me before leaving with Marina. "But don't worry; we will be waiting for you next to the hospital building. We will do our best not to lose you on the road."

Before the ambulance technicians rolled out the gurney, Marina and I kissed each other. The kiss was short, but it seemed like it would last forever. Paramedics moved down the depth of the hospital corridor and disappeared, and with them disappeared the hope that had never left my heart from the moment when thirteen years ago Marina carelessly told me that a radiologist had called her about a suspicious lesion in her breast. Never-ending hope was now replaced with a feeling that I must submit to fate and must be involved in necessary activities. At the same time, I tried not to think about what awaited my dear friend in the near future.

The Last Destination Is Reached

It was late at night on October 25, 2018, twelve days before Marina's death, when the ambulance reached the building where the JourneyCare hospice was located. A security guard of the building allowed me to park illegally before the building and soon I was at the hospice unit. When I arrived, the ambulance team had just brought Marina on a gurney in the hospice room. My inner tension from grim thoughts of what awaited Marina and me in the near future was lifted when a Filipino nurse and an African-American nurse's aide came toward us. These professional women were the embodiment of human care in action. The next day, I found that in this hospice, dedicated to relieving the suffering of patients on the way from life, reigned the atmosphere of love and care toward their patients. Using a tender and warm tone of voice, which I could not call anything other than respectfully maternal, both the nurse and the nurse's aide maintained conversation with my wife. The caregivers' attitude toward Marina and toward me, her husband, was as if we were all members of the same closely related family. They explained to us different details of the new environment. Unfortunately, as I learned later, one thing they did not explain to me was about parking, which would soon cost me a lot of strength and energy.

Though it was the twilight period of her life, Marina did not lose her genuine life-affirming character. In this critical situation, she had two main concerns: first, to be sure she knew where her mobile phone and charger were, and second, to be sure that the button to call a nurse or nurse's aide was always close to her hand. While Marina was in the hospice unit, she courageously continued to be true to her principle of living one day at a time, not worrying about what tomorrow would bring. Her concentration on the problems of the current day prevented her from the capitulated battle with cancer. Looking at the medics with eyes that did not lose inquisitive interest, with steady attention, she listened to what they explained, sometimes asking them to repeat what she did not clearly understand.

Later I learned that JourneyCare was a large company that rented a whole block of hospital rooms from Rush Hospital. The JourneyCare unit functioned according to its own policies, independent from Rush Hospital, and the entire staff worked for the JourneyCare Company.

The hospice care unit was the last shore where for the patients who were there, the living mystery of human life was transfigured into another reality, the essence of which will always remain a mystery for us who are alive and well. It was obvious that the unit's design was the result of a lot of thought. The main idea behind the design of patients' rooms was respect to people, not only for patients but also for those to whom they were dear—for family members, partners, or friends. The unit had ten rooms or more, and every room was large in size and with high windows. Unknown to me before, the unusual width of the comfortable mattress on the hospital beds was intended to allow caregivers to lie next to the patient and, if desired, hug her or him to exchange the warmth of bodies with those who were on their way to their final destination. The sheets, pillowcases, and blankets were shining with cleanliness, and the floor was without a speck of dust. For family members and significant ones who wanted to spend twenty-four hours with the patient, the room was equipped with a specially designed comfortable bed made from wood that could be easily folded in the daytime. For this foldable bed was available a generous supply of fresh bed linens. When additional linen was required, it was provided without delay and frequently by a nurse who did it with a friendly smile on her face.

Though the health of all the patients in the hospice unit was in critical, untreatable condition, like any other room in the hospital, the hospice rooms were equipped with all possible advanced technological medical equipment.

The designers of the unit were not discouraged that the patients in their rooms might not be physically able to appreciate the environment around them. The design provided maximum comfort and convenience for patients, but most importantly, it underlined the company's respect for the dignity of human life. The remarkable environment of the hospice was not the result of government bureaucratic regulations, but the efforts of those who designed this unit to pay tribute to the sanctity of life for people of all backgrounds, a holiness that even death could not take away.

The attention that was bestowed on Marina on the day of her admission was extraordinary, and I only hoped it would continue. Later in the evening, when Marina was securely accommodated in her bed, a nurse asked her if she wanted to eat. When Marina replied that she might eat later, the nurse turned and asked me, not a patient but a visitor, the same question, once again proving a sincere regard not only for the patients but for those who were with them.

That night, Marina, exhausted from the process of transfer, was in a deep sleep. I unfolded my caregiver's bed and fell asleep as well. In the morning, Marina's condition had not changed. Her appearance did not reflect why she was a patient in the hospice—her complexion was satisfactory, and her vital signs were normal except for a slightly increased frequency of breathing. She was well oriented in time, space, and situation. But the most remarkable thing continued to be Marina's lucid mind. The situation in which she was, people usually do not think about the external world and do not worry about it. Her most frequent questions were always the same—she asked about the children and whether I was in good shape. After being reassured that everyone in the family was good, Marina was closing herself in her inner world. In peace and quiet, slowly and imperceptibly to the inexperienced eye, Marina floated on the River of Time to the shores of the inevitable outcome of human life.

When the next day came, it was a pleasant relief for me that the nurse and nurse's aide on the day shift were as good and as professional as those on the preceding night shift. I was immensely happy that in this tragic time in her life, Marina was in good hands and my dream to provide for her the ideal care came through. All over her stay, I was convinced again and again that the entire staff of the hospice unit was excellent at fulfilling their assigned responsibilities.

Not too many people, including the majority of medical workers, are able to face the endless daily deaths of their patients and the grief that goes with it day in and day out. It might not be possible to not be affected by the sorrow that goes with the daily loss of human life. Nevertheless, remarkably, not a single member of the staff showed signs of depression related to their unusually demanding work. Just the opposite. All the nurses, nurse's aides, and auxiliary staff were cheerful and friendly. It was obvious that the hospice unit staff was spiritually satisfied with their mission. Figuratively speaking, their hearts shone with a sincere desire to make the last days, hours, or seconds of their patients' predicament as easy as they could. Such an attitude could not be dictated by rules in policy books. In this unique medical entity where nerve-shattering scenes of people parting with their lives took place often more than daily, the medical staff, inspired by their chosen mission, did not lose their strong and inextricable link with the celebration of human life. These truly special people voluntarily chose to help those who were going through the tragic last moments of their lives. They were able to face up to the daily grief and mourning which, because of the nature of their work, they were forced to observe day in and day out. Only special people are able to compartmentalize their work to such a degree that they have the ability to live normal, everyday lives outside their dramatically challenging jobs.

Strength did not leave Marina completely. She still ate little, but with a bit of help, she could walk in slow steps to reach the bathroom.

I did not want to tire her unnecessarily, so I spoke with her as little as possible. Our usual dialogue during the day now was limited to the exchange of several words. In the background of this limited communication between us was Marina's surprising ability to answer telephone calls as if it were her assigned responsibility. As always, she did not want to burden anybody with her problems. Months after her departure, I learned from my relatives, friends, and acquaintances that she had called them from the hospice unit. She was not calling them to say farewell but in order to let them know how much she liked them and how they were important in her life. Inherent in her, deep sense of duty could be proved by how attentive she continued to be toward her mobile phone, with which she did not want to part for a short period of time. She did not let it go from her hand, giving the impression that it was an umbilical cord that united her with the rest of the world she said goodbye to. And another telling detail: until the last days of her life, she did not forget to recharge her phone. She did not ask somebody to do it for her; she was doing it all by herself.

Marina's lack of desire to eat mostly was due to her persistent nausea and heartburn. It was not the chemotherapy now but influence of the progressing malignancy that was incessantly poisoning her body. To counteract her nausea and heartburn, the attending physician prescribed her a new medication, Haldol. This initially was surprising to me. From my experience, I knew that Haldol was an antipsychotic psychotropic medication, but now I learned that this medication was a blessed cornerstone for helping end-of-life patients who were hostages to pain, nausea, and heartburn. To my great relief, after a hospice nurse injected Marina with Haldol for the first time, her nausea and heartburn diminished so much that she was able to tolerate a small amount of food. Of course, for everything good in our life, we might need to pay. The Haldol helped Marina with nausea, but it made her very tired and sleepy. Since then, under influence of Haldol after finishing small amounts of food, she usually tightly closed her eyes, which made it difficult to know if she was asleep or awake.

Over the next few days, I became more familiar with the structure of the hospice. All ten patients' rooms were located radially from the center around the perimeter of a large and spacious grand hall. In addition to the patient rooms, doctors' and administrative offices were located along the perimeter.

A large room on the floor was occupied by kitchen, which by its purpose could be called source of hospitality. This kitchen was unusual and deserves a separate description. The way it functioned showed that the department's designers respected the needs not only of patients but also of their families and all the significant people in their lives who came to the department to say last goodbye to them. While the hospice provided the kitchen with crackers, pastries, and drinks, visitors often contributed their own food, bought mostly from fast food restaurants. Usually these were pizzas, different dishes, mostly with chicken, and all sorts of different sweets. This food was offered not only to the families of the donors but was shared with all the people on the floor. As a rule, visitors of all races, faiths, and ages ate at a long table in the spacious kitchen or in the grand hall.

The huge grand hall of the department was a vast, unique space occupied by members of the medical team and visitors. Along the long circular wall, instead of the traditional centralized nursing station, each of the full-time nurses had their own mini station, all of which were located right at the entrance to the corresponding patient's room. Each of these mini nursing stations was equipped with everything necessary for its functioning, including computers and printers. This unusual floor plan provided immediate access to professional care for patients and their caregivers. In addition to the nursing mini stations located around the perimeter, on the opposite side of the hall were mini stations for nurses' aides. For their work, they had the same technological equipment as the nurses.

Every family and everyone who was close to the patients, regardless of who they were, were united by the same grief in the expected or just-experienced loss of someone they loved and cherished. To ensure maximum comfort for numerous visitors, the hall was furnished with low tables and comfortable armchairs and sofas.

There was no end to the tragedies that took place within the walls of this hospice unit. Since the patient's death could occur at any time of the day and often at night, visiting hours were not limited. Any person close to a patient, who wanted to stay in the department, could remain there as long as they so desired.

To serve the spiritual needs of patients and their loved ones, a chaplain and one or more distinguished volunteers were available during the daytime. They were often seen in the great hall, always ready to offer their help to satisfy the emotional needs of patients and those who came to visit them.

When at some point I returned to Marina's room, she was talking to someone on the phone, tightly squeezing it in her hand. Her telephone conversations were short and did not contain the slightest hint of a complaint. She fearlessly continued to ignore the destructive invasion of her body by metastases; they couldn't break her will.

Even as she was in her critical state, my heroine never stopped feeling obligated to keep in touch with those who were alive and well. She refused to

216

talk about her predicament and reassured those with whom she spoke that her health was a subject that was not worth discussing.

Predictably, if I asked her why she, as always, didn't tell the truth about her status, her answer would have been sober and without bitterness: "People have their own problems, why should I add my own as well. Let them enjoy life."

Whenever Marina was forced to press her call button, the nurse quickly arrived. The cause for her calls was either pain that quickly spread throughout her body or incessant nausea and heartburn. Both of these symptoms required injections of Haldol, doses of which increased from day to day. Haldol always worked. The injection gave her three hours of good respite from the excruciating symptoms, and then she needed a new dose of pain reliever.

During one of these reprieves, a knock on the door woke Marina from her nap. When the door opened, into the room entered a remarkable visitor, Marina's oncologist, Dr. Miller. To come to the hospice unit from the place where she worked and lived must have taken at least an hour, but she had made it. It was a precious visit from a doctor who had helped Marina and me to never lose hope for the better. She indeed was a living embodiment of one of the basic principles of humane medicine, according to which there are times when the doctor may not be able to help the patient, but the patient should feel better after the doctor's visit. Two remarkable women, whose age difference was over thirty years, were looking into each other's eyes, smiling bitterly and in this bittersweet exchange could be read the entire philosophy of human life. Looking at them from the sidelines, I recalled the lines from the popular song of the famous Russian singer, Bulat Okudzhava: "красивые и умные, как боги, и грустные, как жители Земли," translated as "beautiful and wise as gods and sad as inhabitants of the earth." At the end, the women shook hands, but then Marina leaned over to her doctor, and they kissed each other on the cheek.

In the hospice department, as well as on every hospital floor, a medical team, led by the attending physician, arrived usually for the morning round around 9:30 am. Immediately after Marina was admitted to the hospice, the attending physician informed me that soon she would be discharged home, where she would continue treatment at the hospice. However, her condition was progressively becoming worse, and by the fourth day, it became clear that Marina's condition required her to remain a patient in the hospice department.

In the past, I have been hospitalized several times due to my own health problems, but nowhere have I seen so much compassion and attention toward patients as in the department of Marina's hospice.

Unexpected Listeners

The medical team that conducted the morning round usually consisted of six doctors. Before entering the patient's room, they discussed the case from outside, so when they entered the room, they were already well informed about the patient's current situation. When in the room, prior to examining Marina, the attending physician asked her questions, to which, usually after a short pause, she answered with one or two words. Once, with Marina's invitation, when her lack of strength prevented her from answering, I reported on her state of health for the past twenty-four hours.

Not to waste time of busy doctors, I tried to be as brief as possible, but, to my deep amazement, the members of the group were so sincerely interested in what I told about Marina's condition that without any plan I began to share details of her life in the past. I tried to be quick, sincerely suspecting that at any moment the group would stop my story, but, to my surprise, the opposite happened.

With undisguised interest the medics listened attentively to the stories I told them. Not a single member of the group showed even a hint of annoyance or impatience with my narration. On the third or the fourth day, while Marina was lying motionless on her bed, I began to tell the medical team not only stories related to her cancer but also about various telling episodes of Marina's life, which I thought could show how strong, active, and full of life she was when she was healthy. I had no way of knowing if Marina heard what I was saying about her, but I continued to recollect episode after episode, describing who my Marina was in flesh and blood before a devastating disease turned her into motionless and lifeless body. Even when Marina was admitted to the hospice unit, from our home, I brought several memorable photographs I found in family albums. Encouraged by the continuous interest in my stories, I began to illustrate stories about Marina with her photographs. On the faces of current and future doctors, I saw how genuinely they were touched by the contrast between the photographs of the woman they saw and the terminally ill woman in front of them. In the photographs they saw Marina full of energy, humor, and radiant femininity. Her youthful and sometimes mischievous images symbolized cheerfulness, happiness, and health. It seemed to me that the reason for the medical team's interest in life-affirming images was because my stories tore them away from the depressive scenarios that they observed during rotation in the hospice unit and returned them to the real world, where they lived, where they felt happy and cheerful. Every day I told one or more stories from Marina's life. Soon "the push came to shove." The day came when flashbacks about Marina's earlier life began to affect me emotionally, sometimes forcing me to produce an involuntary sob or two in the middle of a phrase.

But I couldn't stop telling my stories, because I felt I owed it to a person, whom I admired with all my heart. I felt a moral obligation to speak of my wife as gratitude for all the love she had given me during the fifty-six years of our union.

I could not stop wondering why the medics wanted to hear my stories about Marina. Perhaps, along with a temporary respite from the tragedy observed in the unit, this helpless body of the woman on the bed, who was leaving this world and who was totally unknown to them before—under influence of my stories about her and accompanying photos—was transforming into a living person in flesh and blood with a vivid, full-blooded character. Who knows, maybe I managed to convey to them what I was able to see--the final result: Marina's spirit triumphed over the depressing picture of human disappearance from the stage of life.

The medical group's time was limited, which explains why despite their incessant attention, I did not receive many questions. One memorable comment came one day when among the medical students there was a beautiful young woman, who--judging by her figure--was in her late pregnancy. Like the rest of the medical team, she listened attentively when I talked about Marina's life.

At the end of my bittersweet story, the attending physician, who had hardly commented before, turned to the pregnant student. "Like you, hearing about our patient, Marina Tsesis, I feel that it is unfair that sooner or later her life ends," he said. "Undoubtfully, the loss of a loved one brings great emotional pain.

"But the cycle of life never ends," he continued, addressing first the group, and then again the pregnant student, "As nobody else, we, representatives of the medical profession, are reminded daily that human life is temporary. We are all leaving this world, and a new generation is coming to replace us. Yes, we humans are mortal, but the life cycle never ends, and soon a new life that now is in your body, your own child, will help us to celebrate the never-resolved mystery of the world in which we live."

The Caregiver Predicament

Before Marina was admitted to the hospice ward, I had no idea that fatigue was a serious problem faced by a person caring for a seriously ill patient. Exhausted by a continuous series of ever-increasing medical problems in the last month and a half before Marina's hospitalization, I constantly felt tired, and in the beginning of the day, I often was forced to take a nap on my visitor's bed.

One of the factors that contributed to my fatigue was my own fault. During Marina's admission procedure, I did not get enough information about parking. Not knowing that the building where the hospice was located had a convenient valet service, I parked my car in the main hospital garage, which was located so far from the hospice unit that when I finally reached Marina's room, I was tired to such a degree that I needed to have rest. My naps were so often interrupted by doctors, nurses, personal visitors, phone calls, and Marina's needs that I was constantly exhausted and sleepy. Regretfully, chronic tiredness and naps took away precious time that I could be spending with my departing wife. On the other hand, there is never enough time to spend with a loved one. Only after a nap of approximately half an hour, I was able to overcome the fatigue and return to my normal self, when I could again be useful for Marina. I was upset by this unusual level of exhaustion, but there was nothing I could do about it.

Feelings are an integral part of the human psyche. In addition to fatigue, the atmosphere among visitors in the hospice was saturated with sadness, emotional pain, and confusion about the impending loss of their dear ones. It was not only the pastor and volunteers who helped the patients and their caregivers cope with their emotions in this most challenging time of their life. A good word and encouragement were offered by practically all the members of the hospice's medical staff. Approaching death of people who were dear to their hearts, the visitors of the unit, especially the family members, were united not only in a sense of grief and mental pain but also in the sense of human solidarity.

Partings

When on October 30, my son's family came to visit Marina, she briefly woke up until the illness pulled her back into its tight shell of oblivion. When she was awake, a sense of duty did not leave her. At these short portions of time, she did her best to meaningfully communicate with visitors who came to visit her. When for the short pieces of time she was free from Haldol's effect, she was true to her desire of performing meaningful actions. In one of those precious short moments, when her mind was lucid between painkillers, she picked up her cell phone and from memory--yes, from memory!--she dialed to two of her friends. In the last days of her life, she hardly spoke to anyone, including me. She saved her energy for the activities that were most important to her. One of such phone calls she made to my brother's ex-wife. After their ugly divorce, Marina did not speak to her for decades.

"Hello, Manya, it's me, Marina," she said in a weak but decisive voice. "Enough, enough of our conflict. It's all over, and I'm calling to wish you all the best." Her energy was enough for no more than a minute of such a conversation.

Our children spent a lot of time at the hospice, leaving late in the evening. From time to time, Sasha, as delicately as he could, tried to engage Marina in a conversation, but she had the strength only for a short answer. Her responses to him consisted of short phrases that were sometimes difficult to understand. On one of the days, it was the sixth day in the hospice unit, when she spent almost the whole day without opening her eyes, before leaving and not expecting that his mother would answer, Sasha gently took Marina's hand and said, "Goodbye, Mama." Unexpectedly, she opened her eyes and answered quietly, "Goodbye, my dear sonny." She said it with such a genuine feeling of maternal love and tenderness that her short remark was more eloquent than if she had said thousand words.

If not for brain metastases, Marina would have lived longer, but these metastases were putting heavy cross on her life. Under the influence of her now quickly progressing malignancies, her inner organs and systems were crashing one after another, but her mind was intact and was never conquered.

Her Last Smile Belonged to a Miniature Horse

Among other altruistic things in the JourneyCare hospice were activities intended to create positive experiences for those who were in the process of departing from the world of sounds, colors, and images. One of such activity was a chance to say farewell to the world of animals. Three days before Marina left this world, to the unit arrived volunteers—three pleasant women who brought with them two friendly Saint Bernard dogs and a miniature horse. That day, Marina had scarcely opened her eyes; somnolent and groggy for hours, she lay motionless and barely said a word. At the time when the volunteers, who brought animals with them, entered Marina's room and approached her bed, she was lying facing the door. Though it appeared that she was in a deep sleep, that did not stop the experienced volunteers. One of them gently touched her hand and quietly pronounced her name.

After the ensuing pause, Marina opened her eyes and carefully looked at what was happening in front of her. Seeing the faces of friendly dogs, she looked at them with clear interest, but when she noticed the miniature horse staying in front of her face, a true smile appeared on her face. It was a real smile, which I had not seen for more than a month. Her lips moved. Her lips moved in an attempt to say something affectionate to the animals, but she did not have enough strength to make her words audible. Then she raised her left hand that had remained motionless for a long time before and extended it. The trained miniature horse patiently offered her snout while Marina tenderly stroked its welcoming fur and wet nose. The smile did not leave her face until the animals left the room. The visit of the animals was a precious gift to Marina; it was also the last entertainment in her life. Thanks to nameless volunteers who for a moment returned her to the beautiful attributes of life; I had a priceless opportunity to see the last smile on the face of my woman.

But Her Last Kiss Belonged . . . to Her Caregiver

Most of the time, while at the hospice unit, I spent at Marina's bedside, while she lay still and silent on her back on her wide king-sized mattress during the last days of her life. For many reasons, mostly emotional ones, I avoided the opportunity to lie next to her, to embrace her, and to breathe the same air with her. This was too difficult for me. Besides, obviously, the sparks of resurrected hope were still alive in me and sharing a bed that was intended specifically for parting with one's dearest persons in life, in this case with my Marina, in my mind, would cut the last threads of my irrational wishful thinking that she would continue to live. Yes, hope dies last. Two days before her last breath, while she was unresponsive and gave up clutching her phone, I sat at her bedside, listening to her weak breathing, tenderly stroking her hand and her hair. Then, without realizing what I was doing--it happened exactly so--I got up from my seat and lay down on the bed next to Marina while she lay on her back. Still not realizing what I was going to do and following a strong subconscious impulse, I leaned over her, and facing her, I began to peer intently into so intimately familiar to me features of her still beautiful face. Then something truly remarkable happened. Suddenly, Marina's lips slightly raised and curled up as if she was ready to kiss my lips. When I realized what was happening, to the moment when I leaned closer to kiss her, a blank expression returned to her.

It was the last kiss of my wife, who was still alive, the last kiss that will never fade from my memory, and this kiss belonged only to me and to nobody else.

Goodbye, My Love, Goodbye . . .

My fearless fighter, my heroine Marina, parted with her temporary earthly existence on the night of November 5, 2018, ten days before she would turn seventy-five. She died with a calm expression on her face. On a rational level, I was ready for her death, and I knew that the way she died in her deep sleep might be the most desirable dream for the majority of people. Thanks to the incredibly humane care at the hospice, she left this world without pain and suffering.

Without hope, life loses its meaning, and this life's inherited imperative to 'never say goodbye to hope' gave birth to a new hope for me, a hope that now my wife was in heaven with angels, especially since she was so worthy of it. After all, when we die, nobody knows what is happening with our very possible immortal soul.

With my son's family at Marina's bedside, I kissed her quickly losing its warmth forehead, and together we said a short prayer.

In the hospice ward, the death of a patient is an everyday occurrence, and those who were on the shift did their best to help me with related formalities in the shortest time. Anticipating the inevitable, I had already made all the necessary preparations at the funeral home. Since death is a daily event in human society, the procedure associated with organizing a funeral was well organized, physically and emotionally helping the surviving family members with extra stress in difficult times.

Following Traditions

Early in the morning, saying our final farewells to the dedicated employees and taking Marina's belongings with us, my family left the hospice unit. While our son, his wife, and my granddaughter Ruth went home, my grandson Ariel, expressed his desire to accompany me, and together with him, I drove straight to the temple since it was time for the morning worship service. Ariel and his sister had attended a Conservative Jewish School for many years where morning prayer was a daily event.

According to tradition in that Conservative Synagogue, each other day of the week the morning prayer service was led by a different member of the congregation. Though after Marina's death, as any other person in my place would be, I was deeply affected physically and emotionally, at this day, I felt a strong moral obligation to lead the religious service assigned to honor the memory of my departed wife. With a prayer book in my hand, I was on my way to the lectern located in front of the room when I felt a light touch on my arm. I turned around and saw that it was my grandson, Ariel.

"Grandpa, can I join you?" he whispered to me.

My God. If I were a king, for such an offer, I would give away half of the kingdom and more.

"Of course," I replied, incredibly moved by his request. "Come with me."

Ariel's presence by my side at this moment had an unforgettable, deeply symbolic meaning for me. I only could imagine how Marina, if she were alive, would react seeing her husband and grandson standing together at the lectern and leading the morning worship service.

When the service was over, and Ariel and I returned home, the small splash joy I had recently experienced was quickly replaced with mental stress and anxiety that took over my psyche and refused to leave me for many days afterward. I felt half paralyzed. Fortunately, Ariel and my friends came to my aid. Together with them, I prepared my dwelling on the traditional Jewish rituals that are supposed to be observed in the family of the deceased. For a while, the grief left me as we covered house mirrors, prepared the low stools, and did other things to begin the Shiva. Shiva, meaning seven, refers to the seven-day period of mourning by the immediate family of the deceased.

When everything was prepared for Shiva, Ariel and my friends left me. A deep grief again took possession of my soul. I was totally devastated, extremely exhausted, and empty inside. Above all, the most bothering symptom of my grief was a state of irrational anxiety that, despite all continuous efforts, I could not get rid of. I fully realized that after fifteen years of illness and thirteen years of cancer treatment, the loss of my wife should not be unexpected, but my subconscious, like waves that crash the shore, was continuously hitting me inside with heavy and strong waves of emotional pain.

Fifty-Six Years of a Honeymoon

Marina passed away on a Thursday. Ancient Jewish tradition says that the funeral of the deceased must take place as early as possible before the coming Shabbat, i.e., before Saturday. Following this religious requirement, Marina was buried on Friday, one day after her death. Prior to the interment, there was a farewell ceremony in the synagogue that Marina and I had attended for almost forty years. The sanctuary where the ceremony took place was filled with people.

My son and grandchildren gave poignant and touching speeches where they talked about how important their grandmother was in their lives. The same sentiment was repeated in speeches given by members of our extended family and by two rabbis. Trying to be short but meaningful in my speech, I tried to convey what was in the depth of my heart. The most memorable I could come in my speech was that what I had experienced during fifty-six years of life with Marina actually was not a marriage but fifty-six years of a honeymoon. Though this long honeymoon came to an end, memory of it will live forever.

Last Goodbye . . .

When the ceremony was over, all that was left for me to do was to sit next to the coffin holding my wife body while the funeral company car was heading to the cemetery. A surprisingly large number of people came to the funeral—close relatives and all kinds of friends and acquaintances. Neither Marina, when she was alive, nor I had ever thought she was so popular. Being a truly humble person, she never sought attention from those who surrounded her for its own sake. Just the opposite—she was an extremely modest person, but somehow, she'd been able to be noticeable without any effort on her side. Having a positive self-esteem, she didn't need anyone's approval, and when without hesitation sometimes she expressed her bold opinion, it was for the sake of the cause she was supporting, not from a desire to win an argument or popularity. When she was alive, she minded her own business and did not express any desire to know what other people thought of her. This explains why I was so surprised that she was now given such generous public attention.

The strain of the funeral was so hard on me that I barely remember anything that happened at the cemetery and all those who were coming to my home later. Only thanks to the list provided to me by the registry of funeral homes, later I was able to find out the name of those who honored Marina with their presence.

During the funeral ceremony, my children were around me, supporting me and providing me with the warmth of their hearts. More than one of my close friends, seeing the nervous tension I was in, told me to reduce my mental strain, I must give way to crying and tears. However, then and later, crying and tears were never a way for me to handle the grief that possessed me. Is it right to cry on demand? There are people who easily cry during life's stresses, but I did not belong to them. If I ever do cry, I do it when there are no people around me. Besides, other than easily shedding tears for beautiful music or a poem or the contents of a book, crying for me meant something like immersion in a dark space, which was against my deliberate tendency toward a life-affirming view on human existence. From previous life experience, I knew well that crying would make it even more difficult for me to get out of the darkness I was already in. After Marina's coffin touched the ground, following the established tradition, using a spade, I threw the first soil onto the lid of the coffin, followed by the others who were among willing to take part in this activity. In the middle of this, one of the rabbis sprinkled a packet of soil from Israel into the grave--another ritual.

When the last prayers were heard and the body was buried, everyone went home. On the way home, I sadly realized that the woman who had stood by me almost all my life, and whom I loved more than my own life, would never again stand next to me. I also realized that I am not the first or the last who thinks in a similar situation as I thought at that moment.

Shiva, Seven-Day Ritual

Following the ritual's rules of sitting Shiva, the next three weekdays of mourning services took place at my home in the evening. Once more, I was surprised by the number of people who came to pay Marina their last respects. Though I was doing my best to hide what was happening inside of me, the presence of so many people expressing their sincere condolences was tremendously increasing my own fatigue. Nevertheless, it was still pleasing to see the crowd of visitors who came to visit my house over the next three evenings. Three volunteers, mostly friends from the congregation, prepared generous treats to offer to the visitors after the religious service. It was pleasant and precious for me to see the testimony that Marina had left good memories not only in my heart but also in the hearts of so many other people. One of the most remarkable friends who came to Shiva was Marina's oncologist, the charming Dr. Miller. Even more amazing was that she was accompanied by all five nurses who at different times had taken care of Marina in the doctor's office and in the treatment center.

Once again, I had to be surprised that Marina's sincere efforts to not stand out from the crowd had not prevented her to leave a mark on the hearts of so many people.

Dealing with Grief

After thirteen years of living with Marina as she battled with metastatic cancer, I thought I was emotionally ready for her final exit, but it was far from truth.

As a general pediatrician with forty years of experience specializing in behavior problems, I had met countless situations where I would be surprised that my patients could not solve what appeared to me simple family problems. Now it was my turn to be in their place. Despite all my conscious efforts, finding myself in the similar predicament, I could not escape from three main mental problems—anxiety, depression, and sleeplessness. These issues turned my life into a torment. Fortunately, not for a minute, I lost my ability for self-analysis. I was constantly thinking and aspiring how to rid myself of my all-encompassing dreadful grief. Especially tortuous was my anxiety. I could not drive away from myself a thought that something terribly bad was about to happen to me. This vague feeling did not leave me for many days. When my anxiety reached a high level, I could not stop my teeth from chattering against my will. A persistent feeling of pressure in my head and chest did not stop to torment me. As a physician who had been on call for countless nights, I had never had a problem sleeping. Now it was the opposite. In the past, after a middle-of-the-night call from a patient or a hospital, I would fall asleep the minute the call was over. Now this ability to fall asleep right away after being awakened in the middle of night had deserted me. I started to suffer from insomnia and was unable to fall asleep for the entire night, which drove me to despair. My brain actively resisted sleep, and I could not do anything about it. It was my turn to understand how difficult it was from the outside to understand those who suffered from nothing more than emotional pain. No wonder people so often show sincere surprise when somebody they knew well has committed suicide. "I saw him only yesterday, and he looked absolutely normal. He was smiling and he even told me a joke. I cannot understand it," they say so often after such a tragic event takes place.

What goes on inside the human mind is not possible to understand by the outsider. One song that I heard from my mother says that when somebody smiles, everybody around smiles with him; however, when somebody cries, he cries alone. Being an extrovert, I did not hide the depth of my anguish, and though I did not carry it on my sleeve, I knew that even people who knew me well could not understand what was going on in me. The other thing I learned from grief experience was how fruitless it is to say to a person suffering from emotional pain, something like "Pull yourself together. Stop torturing yourself. Look how beautiful life is!" The reason for the uselessness of such platitudes is that normal people cannot understand that in the majority of cases, normal people who develop mental problems themselves do not enjoy being affected by their problem. More than anyone else they want to resolve their psychological conflict. Another thing is that they don't know how to deal with it.

Gradually my grief entered into the realm of crisis. Despite all my efforts, I could not free myself from the constantly growing anxiety, chest pain, depression, and sleeplessness. One of my female friends, a family therapist from the congregation, connected me with a psychiatrist I'd known well in the past. This talented psychiatrist did his best to help me with his valuable advice and prescribed for me antidepressant-antianxiety medication. I will never know if it was my prejudice against that type of medicine, or my inability to tolerate it, but although I repeatedly tried it, I could not handle it. It made me tired, nervous, and more anxious than I had been before. In addition, when I was taking a psychotropic drug, I experienced a peculiar feeling that I existed in two selves—one, the actual me, and the other, a shadow of myself who could act of its own will. Another mental psychotropic effect on me was a periodic strange sensation that my head had separated from my body and was floating above me on the same vertical level as my torso. After suffering from a week of this deformed, warped image of myself, I stopped the psychotropic medication and decided that the only person in the entire world who could really help me get out of my grief with all its peculiar symptoms was me, myself. After a week of tormenting myself with this deformed, distorted image of myself, I stopped taking psychotropic drugs and decided that the only person in the whole world who could really help me get rid of my grief with all its peculiar symptoms was myself.

Ever since my youth, I had read extensively on the subject of human psychology, and after much research, I had concluded that one of the most plausible explanations for human behavior is so-called psychological masochism, which can be plainly characterized as a paradoxical but scientifically proven tendency by human beings to derive pleasure from displeasure. In my case, it was manifested by becoming obsessed with my grief and--as hard as it is to understand-- derive an unconscious pleasure from it. While I was never fully convinced by Freud's fixation on sexuality as one of the moving forces in human behavior, the teachings of Freud's disciples Edmund Bergler, Karl Menninger, and Theodor Reik about masochism appeared to correspond best to my own appreciation of the secret motives responsible for human behavior.

Thanks to that knowledge, I understood that my grief had gradually become a weapon of torture against myself. Unquestionably, grief is a normal reaction when someone loses the object of one's love and adoration, but if the manifestation of pronounced grief goes on for a long time, it becomes counterproductive, seriously damaging spiritual health of the person. In other words, after the recent loss of a loved one, acute grief is normal and natural, while prolonged, or chronic grief is damaging to a person, depriving its carrier of a productive and happy life. A logical objection to a person's persistent grief is that the soul of their beloved who passed away would undoubtedly be very unhappy that the dear to him or her who is left alive cannot overcome their paralyzing grief and return to a normal, constructive life. For me, it was an indisputable fact that if Marina could see me in my misery, she would not like that I was torturing myself and that I did not return to the natural flow of human life. Countless times during our long marriage, in different ways, she let me know that she was proud that her husband was a productive and creative man, and she wouldn't like it at all if I ever became passive, negative, and weak. I finally realized that despite how difficult it might be, it came time to pull myself off the road to self-destruction paved by my unhealthy grief. That happened three months after Marina's irretrievable trip to Heaven.

Twelve Steps to Help Reclaim Freedom from Chronic Grief

The description of returning from a state of chronic grief to a normal mental state deserves a book of its own, and here I list the main steps that, no doubt, helped me get rid of the paralyzing effects of long-term grief. The longer it lasts, the harder it is to get rid of. Persistent grief, which for some victims can last for many years, is like a drug addiction that becomes an invisible force that steals away the joy of life.

As a result, I came up with twelve steps that have helped me and, I hope, will also help those who want to escape from the protracted heavy grief that interferes with normal life. These steps are good both for those who believe in God and for those who do not believe in God, but nevertheless believe in the high meaning of their lives. The following are the steps that have helped me gradually regain freedom from heavy grief after Marina's death.

1. Those for whom we mourn truly loved us and as such if they were now alive, they would want us to be happy and free from pain. Therefore, we torture ourselves not for the sake of the one we have lost, but out of self-pity.

2. No matter how we honor the memory of those who left us, we must not forget that we continue to live and that our primary existential obligation belongs to ourselves. If we want to be useful for ourselves and for those who are alive and dear to us, we must strive for our own physical and emotional health.

3. No doubt the loss of your beloved is a big tragedy, but the death of all human beings is the universal outcome of our lives, and our grief cannot return them back to us. Knowledge that we are as mortal as the beloved person whom we just lost does not affect our positive outlook on life in general. The knowledge of inevitable mortality does not prevent us human beings from loving life, from enjoying it, and from having children, the future generation of people.

4. In the remarkable verse 30:19 of the Bible's Deuteronomy, it is written, "I have set before you life and death, blessings and curses. Now choose life, so that you and your children may live." The immortal universal wisdom of this passage calls us to be on the side of life, to be constructive, and to value our lives.

5. Self-torture involved in grief cannot change anything around us. Those who surround us cannot feel all the degree of grief of those who are in mourning. Each person who is alive has his own problems to deal with in this life, and we will be lucky if somebody who sees our tears understands and appreciates the degree of our pain.

6. We must not forget when we are in grief that no matter how hard our loss is, situation could be even worse. There is always something that can surpass the grief we have endured. Very important is to remember about positive features of our lives, and that no matter how severe our loss was, the situation still could be much worse than it is now.

7. "And this too shall pass," says the old-as-life-itself maxim. Overcoming emotional pain should be and active, not passive-conscious, process. As a general rule, difficult moments in our lives are temporary. The wheel of fortune turns, and "the sky is blue again."

8. We cannot change the past, as for the future, we have serious limitations to control it. Only in the present we can be truly constructive. Time relentlessly moves forward. Therefore, we must cherish each moment of our life.

9. Grief is like a deep well. The longer the mourning lasts, the deeper the person falls into it and the darker the surroundings become. The only way to overcome the pathological grief is to lead a creative, productive, and meaningful life.

10. There are countless sources of psychological and social help for people who are experiencing overwhelming long-term grief, but the most important of these are the bereaved's own desires, motivations, and efforts to get out of a state of passivity and return to a normal level of activity.

11. The Latin phrase "*Mens sana in corpore sano*" states "A healthy mind in a healthy body." One of the most guaranteed ways to cope with prolonged grief is to care for our health, as well as nutrition, sleep, and exercise.

12. We, the living, believe that ultimately the life of each of us has an inherently high meaning. Those who believe in God and in the immortality of human soul, and those who believe that our individual life is not a blind accident but has a high meaning are internally justified and behooved to change the devastating feeling of grief into a strong desire to celebrate each new day of our life.

Epilogue

To paraphrase the title of John Donne's famous poem "Death, Be Not Proud," Marina's aggressive metastatic cancer cannot be proud; it was unable to force Marina to capitulate, and it never crushed her spirit. In taking her life, cancer destroyed itself.

Marina was diagnosed with cancer in 2005, but the size of her tumor suggested it began at least two years earlier. That means that despite the initial opinion of specialists that she might not be alive in another six months, in total she lived with the extensive metastatic process for fifteen years. The real winner was Marina, who lived thirty times longer than the original prognosis. Most of the time during those fifteen years, she led productive and happy life. The numerous side effects associated with chemotherapy did not prevent her from being herself. She enjoyed life and passed on her love to the whole family, especially to her grandchildren. She did not complain even once that she had cancer, she continued to help friends, she volunteered for many years at her grandchildren's school, she did extensive research on the history of Holocaust documents, she was active in the local religious community, she read many books, she lived in the world of art, and throughout the illness, she did nonstop household chores. Concentrating on current issues, she genuinely took one day at a time, never playing a victim. Except for the last days of her life, she never lost control of the situation she was in. During the many challenging negative events related to her health, she treated them as temporary difficulties, never losing hope for a good outcome.

Yes, Marina lost the battle with cancer, but Marina won the war. Cancer, with its aggressive metastases in all vital organs of her body, could not bring her to her knees. She fought it to the last breath, leading a rich and fulfilling life.

Marina is one of many millions of women with breast cancer who meet the enemy as real warriors, real heroines, who are fighting till the last bullet. It is to them that I dedicate this book. The desire to share with the reader the boundless admiration over countless courageous, strong, and lionhearted women, who are not afraid of meeting a powerful adversary and eventually defeating it in a spiritual battle—this is the true purpose of these memories of a remarkable woman.

THE END

Chicago
February 05, 2019–March 02, 2022

Made in the USA
Monee, IL
09 May 2022

96125511R00140